THE *Hilton* BEDSIDE BOOK

Volume Eight

VOLUME EIGHT

THE

Hilton

BEDSIDE

BOOK

A TREASURY OF *Entertaining Reading*
SELECTED EXCLUSIVELY
FOR THE GUESTS OF *Hilton hotels*

PUBLISHED BY *Hilton Hotels Corporation*

Published by
Hilton Hotels Corporation
THE CONRAD HILTON, CHICAGO, ILLINOIS 60605

Library of Congress Catalog Card No. 52–3786

PREFACE

You are about to have an adventure, a very personal adventure that involves no risks beyond your inability to "put this book down." For those quiet moments in your hotel room —before the start of the day's activities, between engagements, when you're ready for bed but not quite ready for sleep—we are pleased to offer these varied adventures in good reading, *The Hilton Bedside Book*, Volume Eight.

We hope that the wide diversity of reading pleasure contained in this selection of fiction, prose and poetry will echo the reading tastes of our guests, offering not everything for all of you, but several things for each of you.

Make your own diagnosis of a strange case of heartburn in Hortense Calisher's chilling story of obsession, and solve, if you can, John Creasey's little mystery of vanishing vintage cars. Consider two sides of Nature: man endangered by one of nature's born killers, the cougar, and the plight of a rare, endangered species in need of help from men ("The Friend"). Ponder with anthropologists Montagu and Darling some long-held beliefs about our intellects, and allow James Trager to explode a few myths about everybody's favorite subject—food.

Straight or mixed, here are suspense, nostalgia, romance and humor with contributions by some of the world's greatest writers. If the balance is weighted in favor of humor, surely not many will complain.

Don't waste another minute. There's something here for every reader's taste and enjoyment. You may discover a writer who becomes a lifetime favorite, and you may find some observation or grain of wisdom that is just what you need to hear. Read and enjoy.

CONRAD N. HILTON, CHAIRMAN   BARRON HILTON, PRESIDENT
HILTON HOTELS CORPORATION

CONTENTS

BRUCE JAY FRIEDMAN   23 Pat O'Brien Movies   239
*(A surprise ending if
ever there was one)*

Heartburn

Hortense Calisher

The light, gritty wind of a spring morning blew in on the doctor's shining, cleared desk, and on the tall buttonhook of a man who leaned agitatedly toward him.

"I have some kind of small animal lodged in my chest," said the man. He coughed, a slight, hollow apologia to his ailment, and sank back in his chair.

"Animal?" said the doctor, after a pause which had the unfortunate quality of comment. His voice, however, was practiced, deft, colored only with the careful suspension of judgment.

"Probably a form of newt or toad," answered the man, speaking with clipped distaste, as if he would disassociate himself from the idea as far as possible. His face quirked with sad foreknowledge. "Of course, you don't believe me."

The doctor looked at him noncommittally. Paraphrased, an old refrain of the poker table leapt erratically in his mind. "Nits"—no—"newts and gnats and one-eyed jacks," he thought. But already the anecdote was shaping itself, trim and perfect, for display at the clinic luncheon table. "Go on," he said.

"Why won't any of you come right out and say what you think!" the man said angrily. Then he flushed, not hectically, the doctor noted, but with the well-bred embarrassment of the normally reserved. "Sorry. I didn't mean to be rude."

"You've already had an examination?" The doctor was a neurologist, and most of his patients were referrals.

"My family doctor. I live up in Boston."

"Did you tell him—er . . .?" The doctor sought gingerly for a phrase.

One corner of the man's mouth lifted, as if he had watched others in the same dilemma. "I went through the routine first. Fluoroscope, metabolism, cardiograph. Even gastroscopy." He spoke, the doctor noted, with the regrettable glibness of the patient who has shopped around.

"And—the findings?" said the doctor, already sure of the answer.

The man leaned forward, holding the doctor's glance with his own. A faint smile riffled his mouth. "Positive."

"Positive!"

"Well," said the man, "machines have to be interpreted after all, don't they?" He attempted a shrug, but the quick eye of the doctor saw that the movement masked a slight contortion within his tweed suit, as if the man writhed away from himself but concealed it quickly, as one masks a hiccup with a cough. "A curious flutter in the cardiograph, a strange variation in the metabolism, an alien shadow under the fluoroscope." He coughed again and put a genteel hand over his mouth, but this time the doctor saw it clearly—the slight, cringing motion.

"You see," added the man, his eyes helpless and apologetic above the polite covering hand. "It's alive. It *travels.*"

"Yes. Yes, of course," said the doctor, soothingly now. In his mind hung the word, ovoid and perfect as a drop of water about to fall. Obsession. A beautiful case. He thought again of the luncheon table.

"What did your doctor recommend?" he said.

"A place with more resources, like the Mayo Clinic. It was then that I told him I knew what it was, as I've told you. And how I acquired it." The visitor paused. "Then, of course, he was forced to pretend he believed me."

"Forced?" said the doctor.

"Well," said the visitor, "actually, I think he did believe me. People tend to believe anything these days. All this mass media information gives them the habit. It takes a strong individual to disbelieve evidence."

The doctor was confused and annoyed. Well, "What then?" he said peremptorily, ready to rise from his desk in dismissal.

Again came the fleeting bodily grimace and the quick cough. "He—er . . . he gave me a prescription."

The doctor raised his eyebrows, in a gesture he was swift to retract as unprofessional.

"For heartburn, I think it was," added his visitor demurely.

Tipping back in his chair, the doctor tapped a pencil on the edge of the desk. "Did he suggest you seek help—on another level?"

"Many have suggested it," said the man.

"But I'm not a psychiatrist!" said the doctor irritably.

"Oh, I know that. You see, I came to you because I had the luck to hear one of your lectures at the Academy. The one on 'Overemphasis on the Non-somatic Causes of Nervous Disorder.' It takes a strong man to go against the tide like that. A disbeliever. And that's what I sorely need." The visitor shuddered, this time letting the *frisson* pass uncontrolled. "You see," he added, thrusting his clasped hands forward on the desk, and looking ruefully at the doctor, as if he would cushion him against his next remark, "you see—I am a psychiatrist."

The doctor sat still in his chair.

"Ah, I can't help knowing what you are thinking," said the man. "I would think the same. A streamlined version of the Napoleonic delusion." He reached into his breast pocket, drew out a wallet, and fanned papers from it on the desk.

"Never mind. I believe you!" said the doctor hastily.

"Already?" said the man sadly.

Reddening, the doctor hastily looked over the collection of letters, cards of membership in professional societies, licenses, and so on—very much the same sort of thing he himself would have had to amass, had he been under the same necessity of proving his identity. Sanity, of course, was another matter. The documents were all issued to Dr. Curtis Retz at a Boston address. Stolen, possibly, but something in the man's manner, in fact everything in it except his unfortunate hallucination, made the doctor think otherwise. Poor guy, he thought. Occupational fatigue, perhaps. But what a form! The Boston variant, possibly. "Suppose you start from the beginning," he said benevolently.

"If you can spare the time . . ."

"I have no more appointments until lunch." And what a lunch that'll be, the doctor thought, already cherishing the pop-eyed scene—Travis the clinic's director (that plethoric Nestor), and young Gruenberg (all of whose cases were unique), his hairy nostrils dilated for once in a *mise-en-scène* which he did not dominate.

Holding his hands pressed formally against his chest, almost in the attitude of one of the minor placatory figures in a *Pietà*, the visitor went on. "I have the usual private practice," he said, "and clinic affiliations. As a favor to an old friend of mine, headmaster of a boys' school nearby, I've acted as guidance consultant there for some years. The school caters to boys of above average intelligence and is run along progressive lines. Nothing's ever cropped up except run-of-the-mill adolescent problems, colored a little, perhaps, by the type of parents who tend to send their children to a school like that—people who are—well—one might say, almost tediously aware of their commitments as parents."

The doctor grunted. He was that kind of parent himself.

"Shortly after the second term began, the head asked me to come down. He was worried over a sharp drop of morale which seemed to extend over the whole school—general inattention in classes, excited note-passing, nightly disturbances in the dorms—all pointing, he had thought at first, to the existence of some fancier than usual form of hazing, or to one of those secret societies, sometimes laughable, sometimes with overtones of the corrupt, with which all schools are familiar. Except for one thing. One after the other, a long list of boys had been sent to the infirmary by the various teachers who presided in the dining room. Each of the boys had shown a marked debility, and what the resident doctor called 'All the stigmata of pure fright. Complete unwillingness to confide.' Each of the boys pleaded stubbornly for his own release, and a few broke out of their own accord. The interesting thing was that each child did recover shortly after his own release, and it was only after this that another boy was seen to fall ill. No two were afflicted at the same time."

"Check the food?" said the doctor.

"All done before I got there. According to my friend, all the trouble seemed to have started with the advent of one boy, John Hallowell, a kid of about fifteen, who had come to the school late in the term with a history of having run away from four other schools. Records at these classed him as very bright, but made oblique references to 'personality difficulties' which were not defined. My friend's school, ordinarily pretty independent, had taken the boy at the insistence of old Simon Hallowell, the boy's uncle, who is a trustee. His brother, the boy's father, is well known for his marital exploits which have nourished the tabloids for years. The mother lives mostly in France and South America. One of these perennial dryads, apparently, with a youthfulness maintained by money and a yearly immersion in the fountains of American plastic surgery. Only time she sees the boy . . . Well, you can imagine. What the feature articles call a Broken Home."

The doctor shifted in his chair and lit a cigarette.

"I won't keep you much longer," said the visitor. "I saw the boy." A violent fit of coughing interrupted him. This time his curious writhing motion went frankly unconcealed. He got up from his chair and stood at the window, gripping the sill and breathing heavily until he had regained control, and went on, one hand pulling unconsciously at his collar. "Or, at least, I think I saw him. On my way to visit him in his room I bumped into a tall red-headed boy in a football sweater, hurrying down the hall with a windbreaker and a poncho slung over his shoulder. I asked for Hallowell's room; he jerked a thumb over his shoulder at the door just behind him, and continued past me. It never occurred to me . . . I was expecting some adenoidal gangler with acne . . . or one of these sinister little angel faces, full of neurotic sensibility.

"The room was empty. Except for its finicky neatness, and a rather large amount of livestock, there was nothing unusual about it. The school, according to the current trend, is run like a farm, with the boys doing the chores, and pets are encouraged. There was a tank with a couple of turtles near the window, beside it another, full of newts, and in one corner a large cage of well-tended, brisk white mice. Glass cases, with carefully mounted series of lepidoptera and hymenoptera, showing the metamorphic stages, hung on the walls, and on a drawing board there was a daintily executed study of Branchippus, the 'fairy shrimp.'

"While I paced the room, trying to look as if I wasn't prying, a greenish little wretch, holding himself together as if he had an imaginary shawl draped around him, slunk into the half-dark room and squeaked 'Hallowell?' When he saw me he started to duck, but I detained him and found that he had had an appointment with Hallowell too. When it was clear, from his description, that Hallowell must have been the redhead I'd seen leaving, the poor urchin burst into tears.

" 'I'll never get rid of it now!' he wailed. From then on it wasn't hard to get the whole maudlin story. It seems that shortly after Hallowell's arrival at school he acquired a reputation for unusual proficiency with animals and for out-of-the way lore which would impress the ingenuous. He circulated the rumor that he could swallow small animals and regurgitate them at will. No one actually saw him swallow anything, but it seems that in some mumbo-jumbo with another boy who had shown cynicism about the whole thing, it was claimed that Hallowell had, well, divested himself of something, and passed it on to the other boy, with the statement that the latter would only be able to get rid of his cargo when he in turn found a boy who would disbelieve *him*."

The visitor paused, calmer now, and leaving the window sat down again in the chair opposite the doctor, regarding him with such fixity that the doctor shifted uneasily, with the apprehension of one who is about to be asked for a loan.

"My mind turned to the elementary sort of thing we've all done at times. You know, circle of kids in the dark, piece of cooked cauliflower passed from hand to hand with the statement that the stuff is the fresh brains of some neophyte who hadn't taken his initiation seriously. My young informer, Moulton his name was, swore however that this hysteria (for of course, that's what I thought it) was passed on singly, from boy to boy, without any such séances. He'd been home to visit his family, who are missionaries on leave, and had been infected by his roommate on his return to school, unaware that by this time the whole school had protectively turned believers, en masse. His own terror came, not only from his conviction that he was possessed, but from his inability to find anybody who would take his dare. And so he'd finally come to Hallowell. . . .

"By this time the room was getting really dark and I snapped on the light to get a better look at Moulton. Except for an occasional shudder, like a bodily tic, which I took to be the aftereffects of hard crying, he looked like a healthy enough boy who'd been scared out of his wits. I remember that a neat little monograph was already forming itself in my mind, a group study on mass psychosis, perhaps, with effective anthropological references to certain savage tribes whose dances include a rite known as 'eating evil.'

"The kid was looking at me. 'Do you believe me?' he said suddenly. 'Sir?' he added, with a naive cunning which tickled me.

" 'Of course,' I said, patting his shoulder absently. 'In a way.'

"His shoulder slumped under my hand. I felt its tremor, direct misery palpitating between my fingers.

" 'I thought . . . maybe for a man . . . it wouldn't be . . .' His voice trailed off.

" 'Be the same? . . . I don't know,' I said slowly, for of course, I was answering, not his actual question, but the overtone of some cockcrow of meaning that evaded me.

"He raised his head and petitioned me silently with his eyes. Was it guile, or simplicity, in his look, and was it for conviction, or the lack of it, that he arraigned me? I don't know. I've gone back over what I did then, again and again, using all my own knowledge of the mechanics of decision, and I know that it wasn't just sympathy, or a pragmatic reversal of therapy, but something intimately important for me, that made me shout with all my strength—'Of course I don't believe you!'

"Moulton, his face contorted, fell forward on me so suddenly that I stumbled backwards, sending the tank of newts crashing to the floor. Supporting him with my arms, I hung on to him while he heaved, face downwards. At the same time I felt a tickling, sliding sensation in my own ear, and an inordinate desire to follow it with my finger, but both my hands were busy. It wasn't a minute 'til I'd gotten him onto the couch, where he drooped, a little white about the mouth, but with that chastened, purified look of the physically relieved, although he hadn't actually upchucked.

"Still watching him, I stooped to clear up the debris, but he bounded from the couch with amazing resilience.

" 'I'll do it,' he said.

" 'Feel better?'

"He nodded, clearly abashed, and we gathered up the remains of the tank in a sort of mutual embarrassment. I can't remember that either of us said a word, and neither of us made more than a halfhearted attempt to search for the scattered pests which had apparently sought crannies in the room. At the door we parted, muttering as formal a goodnight as was possible between a grown man and a small boy. It wasn't until I reached my own room and sat down that I realized, not only my own extraordinary behavior, but that Moulton, standing, as I suddenly recalled, for the first time quite straight, had sent after me a look of pity and speculation.

"Out of habit, I reached into my breast pocket for my pencil, in order to take notes as fresh as possible. And then I felt it . . . a skittering, sidling motion, almost beneath my hand. I opened my jacket and shook myself, thinking that I'd picked up something in the other room . . . but nothing. I sat quite still, gripping the pencil, and after an interval it came again—an inchoate creeping, a twitter of movement almost *lackadaisical,* as of something inching itself lazily along—but this time on my other side. In a frenzy, I peeled off my clothes, inspected myself wildly, and enumerating to myself a reassuring abracadabra of explanation—skipped heartbeat, intercostal pressure of gas—I sat there naked, waiting. And after a moment, it came again, that wandering, aquatic motion, as if something had flipped itself over just enough to make me aware, and then settled itself, this time under the sternum, with a nudge like that of some inconceivable foetus. I jumped up and shook myself again, and as I did so I caught a glimpse of myself in the mirror in the closet door. My face, my own face, was ajar with fright, and I was standing there, hooked over, as if I were wearing an imaginary shawl."

In the silence after his visitor's voice stopped, the doctor sat there in the painful embarrassment of the listener who has played confessor, and whose expected comment is a responsibility he wishes he had evaded. The breeze from the open window fluttered the papers on the desk. Glancing out at the clean, regular façade of the hospital wing opposite, at whose evenly shaded windows the white shapes of orderlies and nurses flickered in consoling routine, the doctor wished petulantly that he had fended off the man and all his papers in the beginning. What right had the man to arraign *him?* Surprised at his own inner vehemence, he pulled himself together. "How long ago?" he said at last.

"Four months."

"And since?"

"It's never stopped." The visitor now seemed brimming with a tentative excitement, like a colleague discussing a mutually puzzling case. "Everything's been tried. Sedatives do obtain some sleep, but that's all. Purgatives. Even emetics." He laughed slightly, almost with pride. "Nothing like that works," he continued, shaking his head with the doting fondness of a patient for some symptom which has confounded the best of them. "It's too cagey for that."

With his use of the word "it," the doctor was propelled back into that shapely sense of reality which had gone admittedly askew during the man's recital. To admit the category of "it," to dip even a slightly co-operative finger in another's fantasy, was to risk one's own equilibrium. Better not to become involved in argument with the possessed, lest one's own apertures of belief be found to have been left ajar.

"I am afraid," the doctor said blandly, "that your case is outside my field."

"As a doctor?" said his visitor. "Or as a man?"

"Let's not discuss me, if you please."

The visitor leaned intently across the desk. "Then you admit that to a certain extent, we *have* been—?"

"I admit nothing!" said the doctor, stiffening.

"Well," said the man disparagingly, "of course, that too is a kind of stand. The commonest, I've found." He sighed, pressing one hand against his collarbone. "I suppose you have a prescription too, or a recommendation. Most of them do."

The doctor did not enjoy being judged. "Why don't you hunt up young Hallowell?" he said, with malice.

"Disappeared. Don't you think I tried?" said his vis-à-vis ruefully. Something furtive, hope, perhaps, spread its guileful corruption over his face. "That means you do give a certain credence—"

"Nothing of the sort!"

"Well then," said his interrogator, turning his palms upward.

The doctor leaned forward, measuring his words with exasperation. "Do you mean you *want* me to tell you you're crazy!"

"In my spot," answered his visitor meekly, "which would you prefer?"

Badgered to the point of commitment, the doctor stared back at his inconvenient Diogenes. Swollen with irritation, he was only half conscious of an uneasy, vestigial twitching of his ear muscles, which contracted now as they sometimes did when he listened to atonal music.

"O.K., O.K. . .!" he shouted suddenly, slapping his hand down on the desk and thrusting his chin forward. "Have it your way then! I don't believe you!"

Rigid, the man looked back at him cataleptically, seeming, for a moment, all eye. Then, his mouth stretching in that medieval grimace, risorial and equivocal, whose mask appears sometimes on one side of the stage, sometimes on the other, he fell forward on the desk, with a long, mewing sigh.

Before the doctor could reach him, he had raised himself on his arms and their foreheads touched. They recoiled, staring downward. Between them on the desk, as if one of its mahogany shadows had become animate, something seemed to move—small, seal-colored, and ambiguous. For a moment it filmed back and forth, arching in a crude, primordial inquiry; then, homing straight for the doctor, whose jaw hung down in a rictus of shock, it disappeared from view.

Sputtering, the doctor beat the air and his own person wildly with his hands, and staggered upward from his chair. The breeze blew hypnotically, and the stranger gazed back at him with such perverse calm that already he felt an assailing doubt of the lightning, untoward event. He fumbled back over his sensations of the minute before, but already piecemeal and chimerical, they eluded him now, as they might forever.

"It's unbelievable," he said weakly.

His visitor put up a warding hand, shaking it fastidiously. *"Au contraire!"* he replied daintily, as though by the use of another language he would remove himself still further from commitment. Reaching forward, he gathered up his papers into a sheaf, and stood up, stretching himself straight with an all-over bodily yawn of physical ease that was like an affront. He looked down at the doctor, one hand fingering his wallet. "No," he said reflectively, "guess not." He tucked the papers away. "Shall we leave it on the basis of—er—professional courtesy?" he inquired delicately.

Choking on the sludge of his rage, the doctor looked back at him, inarticulate.

Moving toward the door, the visitor paused. "After all," he said, "with your connections . . . try to think of it as a temporary inconvenience." Regretfully, happily, he closed the door behind him.

The doctor sat at his desk, humped forward. His hands crept to his chest and crossed. He swallowed, experimentally. He hoped it was rage. He sat there, waiting. He was thinking of the luncheon table.

Advice to Youth

Mark Twain

Being told I would be expected to talk here, I inquired what sort of a talk I ought to make. They said it should be something suitable to youth—something didactic, instructive, or something in the nature of good advice. Very well. I have a few things in my mind which I have often longed to say for the instruction of the young; for it is in one's tender early years that such things will best take root and be most enduring and most valuable. First, then, I will say to you, my young friends—and I say it beseechingly, urgingly—

Always obey your parents, when they are present. This is the best policy in the long run, because if you don't they will make you. Most parents think they know better than you do, and you can generally make more by humoring that superstition than you can by acting on your own better judgment.

Be respectful to your superiors, if you have any, also to strangers, and sometimes to others. If a person offend you, and you are in doubt as to whether it was intentional or not, do not resort to extreme measures; simply watch your chance and hit him with a brick. That will be sufficient. If you shall find that he had not intended any offense, come out frankly and confess yourself in the wrong when you struck him; acknowledge it like a man and say you didn't mean to. Yes, always avoid violence; in this age of charity and kindliness, the time has gone by for such things. Leave dynamite to the low and unrefined.

Go to bed early, get up early—this is wise. Some authorities say get up with the sun; some others say get up with one thing, some with another. But a lark is really the best thing to get up with. It gives you a splendid reputation with everybody to know that you get up with the lark; and if you get the right kind of a lark, and work at him right, you can easily train him to get up at half past nine, every time—it is no trick at all.

Now as to the matter of lying. You want to be very careful about lying; otherwise you are nearly sure to get caught. Once caught, you can never again be, in the eyes of the good and the pure, what you were before. Many a young person has injured himself permanently through a single clumsy and ill-finished lie, the result of carelessness born of incomplete training. Some authorities hold that the young ought not to lie at all. That, of course, is putting it rather stronger than necessary; still, while I cannot go quite so far as that, I do maintain, and I believe I am right, that the young ought to be temperate in the use of this great art until practice and experience shall give them that confidence, elegance, and precision which alone can make the accomplishment graceful and profitable. Patience, diligence, painstaking attention to detail—these are the requirements; these, in time, will make the student perfect; upon these, and upon these only, may he rely as the sure foundation for future eminence. Think what tedious years of study, thought, practice, experience, went to the equipment of that peerless old master who was able to impose upon the whole world the lofty and sounding maxim that "truth is mighty and will prevail"—the most majestic compound fracture of fact which any of woman born has yet achieved. For the history of our race, and each individual's experience, are sown thick with evidence that a truth is not hard to kill and that a lie told well is immortal. There in Boston is a monument of the man who discovered anesthesia; many people are aware, in these latter days, that that man didn't discover it at all, but stole the discovery from another man. Is this truth mighty, and will it prevail? Ah no, my hearers, the monument is made of hardy material, but the lie it tells will outlast it a million years. An awkward, feeble, leaky lie is a thing which you ought to make it your unceasing study to avoid; such a lie as that has no more real permanence than an average truth. Why, you might as well tell the truth at once and be done with it. A feeble, stupid, preposterous lie will not live two years—except it be a slander upon somebody. It is indestructible, then, of course, but that is no merit of yours. A final word: begin your practice of this gracious and beautiful art early—begin now. If I had begun earlier, I could have learned how.

Never handle firearms carelessly. The sorrow and suffering that have been caused through the innocent but heedless handling of firearms by the young! Only four days ago, right in the next farmhouse to the one where I am spending the summer, a grandmother, old and gray and sweet, one of the loveliest spirits in the land, was sitting at her work, when her young grandson crept in and got down an old, battered, rusty gun which had not been touched for many years and was supposed not to be loaded, and pointed it at her, laughing and threatening to shoot. In her fright she ran screaming and pleading toward the door on the other side of the room; but as she passed him he placed the gun almost against her very breast and pulled the trigger! He had supposed it was not loaded. And he was right—it wasn't. So there wasn't any harm done. It is the only case of that kind I ever heard of. Therefore, just the same, don't you meddle with old unloaded firearms; they are the most deadly and unerring things that have ever been created by man. You don't have to take any pains at all with them; you don't have to have a rest, you don't have to have any sights on the gun, you don't have to take aim, even. No, you just pick out a relative and bang away, and you are sure to get him. A youth who can't hit a cathedral at thirty yards with a Gatling gun in three-quarters of an hour, can take up an old empty musket and bag his grandmother every time, at a hundred. Think what Waterloo would have been if one of the armies had been boys armed with old muskets supposed not to be loaded, and the other army had been composed of their female relations. The very thought of it makes one shudder.

There are many sorts of books; but good ones are the sort for the young to read. Remember that. They are a great, an inestimable, an unspeakable means of improvement. Therefore be careful in your selection, my young friends; be very careful; confine yourselves exclusively to Robertson's Sermons, Baxter's *Saint's Rest, The Innocents Abroad,* and works of that kind.

But I have said enough. I hope you will treasure up the instructions which I have given you, and make them a guide to your feet and a light to your understanding. Build your character thoughtfully and painstaking upon these precepts, and by and by, when you have got it built, you will be surprised and gratified to see how nicely and sharply it resembles everybody else's.

1923

The Cougar Does Attack

Don D. Ellis

On a hot August morning in 1958 the telephone got me out of bed at 4 o'clock, about the time there was light enough to see by. The call was from my friend Vern Cousins at the hamlet of Peachland, 19 miles away from my home in Kelowna, British Columbia. Vern was excited.

"Three cougars are playing behind the schoolhouse," he blurted. "Look like an old female and two young ones, but the young ones are almost full-grown. Can you get over here with Red right away?"

"Soon as I pull my pants on," I promised.

"Well, hurry," Vern urged. "School will be starting in two weeks, and we don't want them around then. I'd go with you, but I'm sick with flu."

I didn't take time to put up a lunch. With the weather as

hot as it was, Red would tree the cats in a hurry or he'd quit and come back. Either way, the hunt wouldn't last long.

I have never liked to turn a cougar dog loose on bare ground, no matter what the weather, and this certainly was no day for a hunt. But I felt I had no choice. I was a game warden with the British Columbia Fish and Wildlife Branch. I put in 27 years as a warden before I retired in 1965. Predator control was part of the job, and in this case I had to agree that Cousins had reason to be worried. I knew of too many cougar attacks on children to trust a family group of them around a schoolyard.

I also knew that once word got around, everyone in the community would want these three cats done away with. It was a chore I was duty-bound to take care of.

I was at Vern's house in half an hour. He didn't feel well enough to come outdoors, but he opened a window and pointed to a tree up the steep hill in back of the school.

"They went out of sight past that tree about fifteen minutes ago," he told me.

If I had any doubts, Red settled them when we got to the tree. The dog was a 12-year-old Redbone, the greatest cougar hound I ever owned, and when he told me something, I knew I could believe him. He put his nose to the ground now, rolled out a long mournful bay, and lunged against his collar, begging to go.

The track was perfect for running, but on such a hot morning the scent would fade quickly. In my excitement and haste I blundered. I unsnapped Red's leash, and he was out of sight by the time I got my rifle out of the car. I figured I was going to gather in a cougar pelt, maybe three of them, in short order.

Only then did I realize, with a sinking feeling in the pit of my stomach, that I had let the dog go without buckling on the small brass sleighbell I always put on him when he ran a cougar track.

There was good reason for that bell. As I explained in my story "Hound Man's Dream," the big cats have very little fear of a dog that runs silently. It's barking that puts them to flight and sends them up a tree. Let a hound overtake a cougar without giving tongue, and the cat is likely to turn and kill the dog on the spot. The bell eliminates any chance that the hound will take the cat by surprise and get himself done in.

I was a worried cougar hunter when I started up the hill behind Red that morning. The old female cat with young would be very likely to pick a fight.

The cats followed a dirt road for a way, then turned onto a cattle trail that led toward a mountain half a mile away. My only hope was that Red would overtake them while he was still making plenty of music.

He didn't make it. The cattle trail went up a bare rocky slope, and the dog stopped baying. Then the thing happened that I was dreading. Where a tree had fallen across the trail, the two young cougars went on but the old girl waited in ambush. When Red scrambled over the tree she laid his throat open with one swipe of a paw. I found the hound dead when I got there.

That was the last I heard of those three cats. They never caused any trouble, and so far as I know they were not seen in that neighborhood again—which was just as well for everybody concerned, themselves included.

Although cougars normally prefer to avoid adult humans, the situation is a bit different with children. A cougar recognizes children for what they are and has little fear of them. And there are other conditions under which he is not to be trusted, such as when he comes into a yard and kills a dog or livestock, or takes to prowling at the edge of a town or close to a farmhouse. He can be treacherous then.

I recall a case in which two small cougars came out of the hills at Winfield, 20 miles north of Kelowna, invaded the schoolyard, and fed on scraps left from the children's lunches. A neighbor chased them up a tree and shot them. Investigation revealed that the cats were youngsters about eight months old that had lost their mother and were having a hard time making out on their own. If they'd got a little bigger they'd have been the kind not to be trifled with.

In the winter of 1970 we had another occurrence involving a hungry cougar near Kelowna. Snow was deep, and game animals were all short of food. An old cougar that had lost most of its teeth came into a farmyard and killed a pig at night. Too hungry or weak to carry its kill off, it fed in the yard. A local hunter tracked it with his hounds and shot it the next morning. A cougar as close as that to starvation must be considered dangerous to man.

On the rare occasions when the big cat does molest humans, if all the circumstances are known there is almost always some special reason. The cougar may be starving because game is scarce. It may have been wounded by a hunter or disabled by porcupine quills, or maybe it's too old to kill its natural prey. Or a man may get too close to the cat's kill or blunder across a female with young.

John Lesowski, a fellow British Columbia game warden, has described three cougar attacks that seemed to have been unprovoked. But each time, when the whole story was told the reason was plain enough.

One of those attacks happened in the Horsefly Lake area in 1942. That cat crashed through thick brush toward Jack Carson, a trapper, broke into the clear at three or four paces, and jumped for the man's face. Carson saved himself by dodging behind a tree and killed the cougar with one shot. It was a big female, and when he skinned her he found the udders full of milk. The trapper believed that her kits were nearby and that she had jumped him to protect them.

On Vancouver Island in 1953 a fisherman was picking up wood for his cooking fire when he saw a cougar crouched behind a log. It spit at him and then sprang. His partner came to the rescue and killed the cat with an ax. A small animal, gaunt and thin, it was on the verge of starvation.

In the third attack Lesowski told about, a 15-year-old boy was helping a rancher build fence in the Clinton area when a cougar stalked the boy from behind a clump of brush and leaped onto his back. The rancher fought the animal off with a pocket knife, but not before it had clawed the boy badly.

Lesowski and another conservation officer hunted that cat down. It was a female that should have weighed around 125 pounds. Instead she weighed 70. Again it was plain that hunger had driven her to the attack.

In his story, "The Man Who Feeds The Trumpeters," Jack Turner told of a cougar that came into his yard at Lonesome Lake and threatened his seven-year-old daughter. Almost certainly the child was saved from attack only because she was inside a henhouse and kept the door shut.

Turner killed the cat after it took refuge in his log barn. Its throat, face, and mouth were stuck full of porcupine quills.

"That was the gauntest and hungriest-looking animal I had ever seen," Turner said.

Those are typical cases of cougar attack. We had one of a slightly different kind in the Kelowna district last winter. A fisherman walking back to his car on the McCullough Lake road noticed a flock of magpies and went into the brush to investigate. A cougar came for him but stopped a few feet away, crouching and lashing its tail from side to side. The man backed off, and the cat did not press its attack.

When hunters went to the spot the next day they found the cat's kill, a deer, behind a log. The fisherman had trespassed too close.

It's not too unusual for one of the big cats to fail to finish what it starts when it tackles a man. I have known several instances in which a cougar bluffed hard without really trying to kill or injure its victim. I think the cats have a little too much fear of humans, and their nerve fails at the last second. They just don't unleash the deadly ferocity they show on deer and other game.

One of the strangest cases of that kind I ever heard of happened in Kootenay National Park just west of the Alberta–British Columbia border in June of 1970.

A Calgary woman, a member of a climbing-and-hiking club, was on a hike in the park with several companions. On a trail by herself, she suddenly saw a cougar running at her down a steep slope. She tried to get her backpack off and use it as a shield, but the cat gave her no time for that. It grabbed her by an arm and knocked her down. She managed to get the pack between herself and the cougar and then regained her feet. Blood was running from deep gashes above her elbow.

She then began to talk to the cougar as she would talk to a pet, and at the same time started to back slowly away. The animal snarled each time she moved but did not renew its attack. The woman kept backing off, talking quietly all the while. The cougar padded ahead a few steps, smelled the blood on the ground, and lay down, watching her.

The stalemate lasted about half an hour, until the victim heard other members of her party approaching and yelled for help. When they answered with whistles the cat ran off. The woman believed that the cougar was a female that had young nearby.

One thing I'm sure of: that cat did not really want to kill the woman. Treated by a doctor, she was able to go back to her office job the next day. I have seen countless cougar kills of deer and even full-grown moose, and I know what the big cat is capable of. If that one had decided to kill the woman, nothing could have saved her. And if the attack had been a determined one, at best she would not have gone back to work the next day or for many weeks.

The cougar has one habit that makes people think of him as a spooky character. He likes to trail humans, as furtively as he trails deer or other game. I'm not sure whether he does it out of curiosity, or from a desire to close in that he does not quite dare to carry out. But it has happened to me plenty of times.

When I was a boy in my teens we lived back in the bush 30 miles from Kamloops and 15 miles from the nearest country store, where my brother and I had to go once a week for supplies and mail. There was no road, so we walked cross-country and often didn't make it home before dark.

Cougars were very plentiful in that area then. Twice on moonlit nights my brother and I looked behind us and saw one skulking silently along on our track. Each time, when we stopped, it stopped. When we walked on, it followed again. We weren't much afraid (maybe we should have been), and by the time we had been trailed a while it got to be almost a game of tag between us and the cat.

The same thing has happened to me on many occasions since. Following my own track home after days in the hills, I have found where a cougar had trailed me for a mile or more.

I recall one trip when I stopped for a mug-up and built a fire. The day was not too cold, and I was tired. After eating my lunch I stretched out for a nap beside the fire. When I was ready to leave I walked my own backtrack for 100 yards and found that a big cougar had followed me and had sat in the snow—only a few yards away—and watched me eat and sleep. He could have killed me before I knew what was happening.

I know plenty of men unfamiliar with cougar ways who

would be scared half to death by such an experience, but I still don't think I was in any real danger. I have spent most of my life in the woods in cougar country, and not once has one of them threatened me.

In my years with the Fish and Wildlife Branch, I killed as many cougars as any hunter I know about. Some were hunted for sport, but more were shot when they came so near human dwellings that people became alarmed or when they took to killing stock. I must add, too, that in my early years as a game warden the big cats were on the wanted list as predators, and it was our job to destroy them if we could.

I'm glad to see that attitude changing. Cougars do kill deer, elk, and moose, but they have shared a common range with these animals for a long time without harming the game supply. Except in a very few cases where the cats became overabundant, I have never known them to damage a healthy deer herd.

For one thing, cougars eat what they kill. If their prey is too much for one meal, they cover what is left with leaves or snow and come back to it and feed periodically until it is gone. They'll hang around a deer or elk kill for a week or more, and I have seen instances in which other game bedded down within a few yards of the kill, unafraid.

I can't say I ever enjoyed killing the big cats, and some years ago I hung up my guns as far as they are concerned. Any I shoot from now on will be shot with a camera.

I rate the cougar as one of the best game animals we have. I'd like to see him protected under hunting laws, taken only as game, and destroyed by predator hunters only when there is real need.

The loss of Red that hot morning at Peachland led to a strange sequel, and in the end, to one of the most exciting hunts I ever had.

I was left a cougar hunter without a dog. I might as well have been handcuffed and blindfolded. I went to Jim Farquharson, a friend at Kamloops who kept good hounds, and he gave me a big rangy Bluetick one-year-old. Lad was the biggest hound of his age I had ever seen. I told Jim that when the dog got his growth I'd be able to ride him up the hills.

As soon as the first snow came I took Lad out to test him on bobcats. He took the first track we found and ran it like forked lightning. He had a good voice, and he put the cat up a tree within about 600 yards. It was quite a performance for a pup. He stayed at the tree, too, and I told myself I had the makings of another great hound.

Then I got the surprise of my life. I walked up to the tree, and the dog started to growl, the hair on his neck stood up, and he came for me, as mean as a cornered wolf. I had never seen a hound behave that way before.

I kicked him off and shot the bobcat out of the tree with my .22 pistol. Lad jumped it the instant it hit the ground, and I couldn't get it away from him. Bobcat pelts were bringing as much as $30 at the time, but when I finally got Lad under control this one wasn't worth skinning. I found myself wondering whether my young hound was going to take his work a little too seriously.

Not long after that I got my first chance to try him on a cougar. A complaint came in of a big cat seen on a road, again near Peachland. I found the track, belled the dog, and kept him on leash. We'd walked about a mile when we jumped the cat from its bed.

Lad seemed anxious to go, but I noticed that his tail was tucked between his legs. When I unleashed him he took the track in a hurry and gave plenty of tongue. But he followed it only 300 yards before coming back to me on a dead run, and nothing could persuade him to take it again.

I concluded then that Lad's bloodline wasn't all it should have been. Young hounds that do not come from good hunting stock are likely to behave that way when they start on cougar.

I was getting discouraged with Lad. I phoned Al Frisby, a game warden at Vernon, and asked for a hand. Al was hunting then with a small Yellow Labrador retriever that was known all over the area as a great cougar dog. I asked for a chance to run my hound with his Shadow.

He called me a few evenings later to say that a logger had reported a deer freshly killed by a cougar, and he was going after the cat the next morning. I'd be welcome to join him. I was at his house at daylight.

It was a clear winter morning with six inches of fresh snow on the ground, just right for what we wanted to do. Two 13-year-old boys were going with us: Al's son Brian and his friend Vern Glenn, the son of the logger who had reported the kill.

We found the deer kill that had been reported to Al, but to our surprise it was the work of not one cougar but three. They were all full-grown, too. They had come back and fed in the night, and we agreed we'd have an easy hunt.

We followed the tracks for three miles, with the dogs on leash. The cougars had walked single file, taking their time. We found their bed in a dry, roomy hole under a rock as big as an average house. I had never seen a place that reeked of cat the way that one did.

The cougars heard us coming and took off at a run. Lad went frantic, but his eagerness didn't last long. We let both dogs go, and they were out of sight in minutes. But two or three minutes later they came streaking back with Lad in the lead.

Al and I figured that my hound, being faster, had overtaken the three cats by himself, lost his nerve when they turned on him, and communicated his panic to Shadow. I was all for shooting him on the spot, but Al talked me out of it.

While we were debating what to do, I happened to recall a recent conversation I'd had with an Indian at Kelowna who often killed cougars without the help of a dog.

"Dog no good, he run deer," he had told me. "I find cougar track, I follow him maybe all day. When I jump cat I run, make lots of talk. He go up tree right away. No dog to feed."

Al and I decided to try it. We put the dogs back on leash and followed the cougars toward the top of the mountain. They must have known we were after them, but they showed little concern. We finally got close.

"It's now or never," I told Al. We let the dogs go again, and they lit out. Al and I and the two boys stayed right on their heels, howling like banshees.

We caught the cats on an open flat with few trees. Maybe for that reason, they did something I'd never known adult cougars to do (and I've never heard of it since). All three went up the same tree, a big thick fir. Usually a cougar group scatters in all directions when hounds close in.

One of these three cats was no more than six feet from the ground, lying on some branches as if to hide from the dogs. The second was standing on two large limbs 10 feet higher, and 10 feet above that one the third was braced in a fork. They made quite a picture.

It's been my experience, incidentally, that a treed cougar doesn't like to climb any higher than he has to, maybe because he prefers to be close to the ground if he has to jump. My son Bud and I often carry slingshots and few pebbles on our hunts, for moving cats up to a better location for pictures.

I remember one hunt on which a young partner and I came upon an old female and three youngsters that my dog had treed in a spruce swamp. I left my companion under a big spruce, where the three kits were keeping the dog occupied, while I went to look for the old lady.

The spruce was draped with the long, trailing, gray lichen that we call moose moss. The young hunter reached up and pulled down a strand, and reached for another. Unknown to him, the female cougar was lying on a thick branch just over his head, and he grabbed her dangling tail with a handful of moss. She ripped out a hair-raising snarl, and I've never seen anybody leave a spot faster than he did.

But back to the three adult cougars in the same big fir. Frisby and I shot out two of them. The third, the one highest in the tree, sailed out in a long arching, downhill leap and raced off. The dogs treed it again after a very short run, and that finished the hunt. Lad had made no trouble, and I hoped he was cured of his bad habits.

A short time after that I had another complaint, one that was not easy to believe. A cougar had prowled up to an isolated farmhouse, put his front paws on a windowsill, and peered in. The tracks proved the story. I could picture him there in the black of night, a great lithe beast, stealthy and mysterious, sniffing the smells of the darkened house, his ears flattened, his long tail twitching.

I went after him with Lad. We found the cougar on the carcass of a deer he had killed, too full of venison for a long chase, and the dog treed him quickly. But when I walked up to the tree and started to put a leash on Lad, he growled and showed his teeth, and I couldn't handle him. I shot the cougar out, and before I could get the hound off the carcass he had torn the skin to ribbons.

I finally went after Lad with a stout club, and he fought like a mad dog. I had to knock him out to get the leash on.

That was the last time I ever hunted with Lad. He was as good a tree dog as I ever had, but more dangerous than any cougar.

As I said earlier, many of the cougars I have killed were hunted down because they appeared to be a threat to humans, either children or grownups. How real is the danger in such cases? Are there any authentic records of the big furtive cats having actually killed people?

Unfortunately the answer to that last question is yes. I

know of three instances, one in the state of Washington, the two others in British Columbia. All three of the victims were young boys.

The Washington attack occurred in 1924 near Malott, a few miles north of the Columbia River. A 13-year-old boy failed to return from an errand at a neighbor's ranch, and searchers found his half-devoured body. Tracks in the snow told what had happened. A cougar had stalked him and struck him down when he ran for a tree, probably intending to climb.

A month later a full-grown female cougar was trapped a few miles away, and in the stomach were found some of the boy's hair, fragments of his clothing, and an empty brass cartridge that he'd had in his pocket.

Twenty-five years later, in 1949, a seven-year-old boy was attacked and killed near Port Alberni on Vancouver Island. The youngster strayed too near a cat that had taken a dog and two raccoons earlier and was watching its kills. That was a typical case of a cougar that had moved close to a settlement and for one reason or another was no longer afraid of humans.

The third victim was struck down last January, in the Lytton district northeast of Vancouver. Twelve-year-old Lawrence Wells was attacked near his home as he crawled out of a culvert in which he and other children had been playing. The boy's father, alerted by his playmates, shot the cougar three times as it dragged Lawrence off, but the boy was dead when the father reached him. Mounties later found the cat wounded in the brush nearby and finished it.

The records leave no room for doubt. The cougar is a magnificent wild animal. But he is also a cat, big and unpredictable. He is not the born killer that many believe him to be. If he were, all the fishermen, hikers, rockhounds, and other unarmed people who roam our hills nowadays—as well as game officers and predator-control men—would lead perilous lives.

But neither is the cougar to be taken lightly when he prowls close to human habitations, and he should never be tolerated where there are children within his reach.

America's Guest

Give me a millionaire with a bad backswing and I can
have a very pleasant afternoon.
> — George Low,
>> *on the subject of survival in golf*

Dan Jenkins

In professional tournament golf the clubhouse veranda can
often be a noteworthy blend of rumble seat, wax museum,
promenade deck, theater wings and courthouse steps. As the
tour moves from one Crystal Rancho Happy Avocado Creek
Country Club to another, the verandas undergo some severe
botanical changes—a palm will beget a pine, or a eucalyptus
will beget an oak—but the human plantlife will remain
practically changeless. Except for the occasional intrusion of

a spectator fully equipped with binoculars, periscope, chair seat, transistor, program, pairing sheet, camera and hot dog, and the almost invariable presence of at least one young female in form-fitting slacks, huge dark glasses and a straw bonnet, the regular veranda standers comprise a remarkably homogeneous and identifiable part of golf. They are the hanging-in, cooling-it businessmen of the game. And as they spread across the lawn, gazing toward the nearest leader board while a tournament progresses, they are not unlike a cluster of military commanders observing the glow of shell-fire from a distant valley.

To almost anyone in the 1960's who knew the difference between a Ben Hogan driver and a shooting stick the faces of these fringe personalities looked as familiar as casual water, but only the true insider was able to identify them by name. There was the stocky, pink-faced man in the dark blazer, his hands usually folded behind him, the one ready with a Sam Snead anecdote or a story about the 1937 Ryder Cup team. That was Fred Corcoran, Snead's lifelong agent and the tournament director of the International Golf Association. There was the tall, blond fellow in the white shoes, a briefcase in one hand and Winnie Palmer's arm in the other. That was Mark McCormack, a Cleveland lawyer and manager of Palmer, Jack Nicklaus, Gary Player and most of the ships at sea. And there were several others, forming a sort of corporate blur, spaced equidistantly among the umbrellas: J. Edwin Carter of the World Series of Golf, Jack Tuthill, the PGA tournament supervisor, Bob Rickey, a Brunswick-MacGregor vice-president, Ernie Sabayrac, an equipment distributor, Bob Drum, a hulking writer, Joe Wolfe, the Wilson clubmaker, Darrell Brown, Palmer's pilot, Doc Giffin, Palmer's personal secretary, Malcolm Hemion, a TV director for ABC, and, finally, the most familiar figure of all, that of a man called Bubble Head, a man who was always there, never doing anything.

On or off the verandas, Bubble Head, or George Low, was (and still is) the stand-around champion of three decades. He is, all at once, America's guest, underground comedian, consultant, inventor of the overlapping grip for a beer can, and, more importantly, a man who has conquered the two hardest things in life—how to putt better than anyone ever, and how to live lavishly without an income.

For thirty years George Low has been the vaguest, most mysterious man in all of golf. Outwardly solemn and immobile, he stands like an urban renewal project on the verandas in a plaid jacket and an open-collared shirt, deeply tanned, granting interviews only to bookmakers and forcing grins only toward those who might seem inclined to buy him lunch or a cocktail. It has been said that if George Low is not on your veranda the tournament simply hasn't started yet. When the Western Open was held at the Field Club in Pittsburgh in 1959, for example, George did not reveal his two hundred forty pounds until the final round, whereupon a friend on the committee scolded him for being tardy and nearly giving the event a bad name.

"Well, you got to understand that a man who don't have to be back to his office for thirty years is sometimes gonna be lax," said George.

The only office that George Low has ever had is the trunk of someone's automobile, preferably a Cadillac, which, if he borrowed it for long began to look like a rummage sale of golf clubs, clothes and photo albums. George has no age. His lungs are one hundred, his stomach is one fifty, and his soul is two thousand, says he. The body has been fifty-four or so for a while. For most of these years, at any rate, George's home has been a car seat, a convertible couch in someone's living room, a roll-away bed in a friend's hotel room, or when he's going good, the vacant wing of a friend's mansion. But always these places have been where the sunshine is—either on or near the PGA tour. He is also very comfortable in Palm Springs, Scottsdale or Miami Beach, whether the tour is in the vicinity or not, or at Saratoga, Santa Anita or Gulfstream.

"I go where some rich guy's got a bed and a kind heart," George says. "Most guys are if-come in this world, but there's a few that ain't phony, and they like having me around. They understand that I got to be where it's warm 'cause I can't afford no overcoat."

To the person who is "strung out," as George puts it, which means he has a steady, respectable job, it may seem that Low's existence is mostly a matter of survival. But George has never thought of it quite that way. On the contrary, George Low has usually lived comfortably, and often far better than the strung-out fellow who rides a commuter train or drives the freeways to work, who is paying off a divan and a Frigidaire and who has to purchase a daily ticket to a golf tournament, not admissible to the clubhouse.

The main reason why George Low has been able to survive in reasonable splendor is that he has one of those personalities that appeal to gentlemen of means. He has a rare sense of humor that makes him one of the superb put-down artists of his time, an unobtrusive manner for being around and not bothering anyone and a crashing honesty, all of which can add up to good company. Aside from these things George knows as much about golf as anyone, and a lot of gentlemen of means like to play golf, apparently while being put down unobtrusively, honestly and without being unduly bothered.

If he *does* have to work he does that on a putting green in Palm Springs or Miami Beach, mainly, where he is apt to putt with a wedge or with his shoe against a wagerer using a putter, and come out all right.

"Put me on a putting green in Miami for a week," says George, "and I'll kill more tourists than the Fontainebleau."

Among the celebrities who have demonstrated that they

enjoy George's company and have, therefore, been his happy hosts, are, just to touch on four different sports, Jimmy Demaret, Willie Shoemaker, Horace Stoneham and Del Miller—a golfer, a jockey, a baseball owner and a harness racing mogul, respectively. George has visited with Stoneham in Phoenix during November, he has spent Christmas with Demaret in Houston and he has devoted a lot of weekday drop-ins to Shoemaker in Los Angeles and Miller in Pennsylvania. It was Paul Grossinger of the resort by that name in the Catskills who once labeled George "America's guest."

"After which he come up with a freebie," says George.

Another associate, Bob Johnson, once the president of Roosevelt Raceway outside New York City, may have summed up George perfectly—at least it delights George—for all of his hosts one evening as Low kept badgering Johnson for another hundred dollars to buy drinks for everyone at a Palm Springs party.

"Just loafing with George is better than having a Dun & Bradstreet rating," said Johnson.

All of this helps make absolutely clear George's uncomplicated philosophy of life, or rather his blueprint for leading a life of ease.

"There ain't no use hanging around a broke 'cause nothing falls off," he says. "The only time I pick up a check is to hand it to somebody."

This, for George, sharply divides the world into two distinct categories of people—those who "come up," or pay, and those who "plead the fifth," or don't pay, when a tab appears.

Since most everyone who knows George knows him well enough to keep his pocketbook either handy or hidden, there are never any surprises or embarrassing situations. If George strolls by you prepare to pay or you prepare to leave. "It's an honor to pick up my check," he says. "How many true celebrities do you know? Anyhow, if you plead the fifth I'll go find a live one somewheres."

Low has a carefully thought out term for the man with a reputation for being something less than a wild spender. A very cautious student of the dollar, George calls him. Like Sam Snead.

"When I dine with Mr. Snead he always suggests that I order as if I was expecting to pay for it myself," says George. "I have known many great destroyers of money, but Mr. Snead is not among them."

Anyone who might happen to stand near George on a veranda at a tournament is likely to be treated to a comic routine. It oozes out naturally from his husky voice and always with a cynical tone. Most of the competitors have learned to feed George straight lines just for the pleasure of picking up a new expression.

Al Besselink came by one day at Pensacola and said, "Loan me fifty, Bubble."

Staring straight ahead at a sheltering palm Low said, "Loaning you money is like sending lettuce by rabbit."

Another time, as George rested himself against the trunk of an elm at Colonial, Billy Maxwell goodnaturedly said, "Wish I had your energy, George."

"I wish I had a rock in each hand," said Low.

When Mark McCormack began packaging and selling Arnold Palmer, a close friend of Low's, in ways that no one had ever thought of before and practically printing money in the process, it gave George a lot of ammunition for his veranda standing. If someone were to ask Low if he had seen McCormack lately George would reply, "Yeah, he was sticking up a supermarket about an hour ago."

Mark learned to approach Low delicately, but it would never do any good. George would only tell McCormack, "Driving your getaway car is the best job in golf."

Bing Crosby once told George, who had insinuated he needed a room during Bing's tournament, that he could probably fix him up at the Del Monte Lodge and probably for a good rate.

"Thanks a lot," said George. "Can I loan you a dime to mark your ball?"

The Crosby has never been famed for drawing large crowds to the Monterey Peninsula for two reasons: it is inconveniently located on a 17-mile drive from Earth, and the weather is nearly always deplorable. When Crosby seemed rather excited one year by what appeared to him to be a better than average turnout Low remarked, "I seen more people on the back of a motorcycle."

Though George might frequently have a hangover gaze about him, his mind remains quick. Roasting in the Las Vegas sun one afternoon during the Tournament of Champions, when it was still being held at the Desert Inn course and when Wilbur Clarke was still alive, George noticed something unusual going up on the scoreboard. Arnold Palmer had just posted a nine, a seven and a five, in that order. Turning quietly to Clarke, Low said, "That's twenty-one. Pay him."

One of the better verandas to stand around on is that of the Augusta National Golf Club during the Masters. It has two big shade trees, some crawling wisteria, a scattering of umbrellas and tables and, always, George Low. He will move from a table to a bench to a tree trunk to a slope in the sun and back again, covering his steps, mumbling comments about the wretched state of the world and how many brokes there are in it. One year George arrived fresh from having spent a weekend sharing a hotel room with a friend, Bob Drum, who was then a writer for the *Pittsburgh Press*.

"How do you like rooming with Drum?" George was asked.

"It's okay," he said. "If you don't mind taking a shower with your money in your hand."

And there was the time at Augusta that George was hearing about Oscar Fraley, a former columnist for UPI, getting into a minor argument in a bar and causing some mild excitement. As the tale was being related by someone who had witnessed it, Fraley happened to stroll by. George interrupted the story and called to Oscar. "I hear you didn't start no fight last night for a change," he said. "Where'd you stay? In a room full of nuns?"

George Low may not have been born bourbon-faced or angry, but he was certainly born "energetically lazy," to use his words. "He was born retired," is the way Jimmy Demaret has put it. The event of George's birth occurred before World War I, that much is known, and not three hundred yards, a stout Nicklaus tee shot, from the pro shop at Baltusrol Golf Club in Springfield, New Jersey.

"I like to say I was born in the 19th hole—the only one I ever parred," Low says.

He was the son of a rather famed Scot, George Low, Sr., who was runner-up for the U.S. Open championship in 1899 and who became the resident professional at Baltusrol. As one of those Scots who came to America to teach the game to an intrigued continent, George, Senior, numbered among his pupils a couple of renowned White House slicers, William Howard Taft and Warren G. Harding.

"There were poor guys like that all around Baltusrol," George remembers. "The Toppings and them kind of charity cases."

Despite the fact that George grew up near the 1st tee of a golf course, he did not try to learn the game until he was fifteen. And this after his father had retired and taken his son back to Scotland. George *had* to play golf in Scotland, he felt.

"What else is there to do over there? Wear a skirt?"

Try as he did to avoid playing golf, two things came naturally to George. A good swing and a deep, nagging feeling about the game. These attributes combined—conspired, more probably—to bring him back to the U.S. in the early 1930's. But in those days George returned as more than just an assistant pro at a variety of clubs in the upstate area of New York. For instance, there was one summer when he was working at a club in the Catskills when he was struck with a get-rich scheme. He found a friend who owned a Ford Tri-Motor airplane and together they dreamed up the idea of shuttling newspapers from the cities to resort areas.

Soon, they decided they could make their business even more profitable by shuttling more than papers. Like booze, this being during Prohibition. And at the same time, on weekends, they staged what could only be described as the world's worst air show featuring George Low parachuting out of the Tri-Motor.

"I didn't exactly jump," he says. "I'd open the door of the plane, and then I'd open the chute and let it pull me out. Who the hell wants to jump if he don't know the chute's gonna open?"

All of this came to an end one cold evening during a shuttle flight when the plane somehow drifted into a small mountain.

"Me and the pilot got out safe, but the booze died," George says.

It was also during these early, formative years that George developed a special fondness for Saratoga and thoroughbred racing itself. In August during the Saratoga meeting, he got acquainted with the sport by becoming a runner, one of those guys who found out what the swells in the box seats wanted to wager on a race and then ran to the betting tables to get it down for them.

"I knew all the rich guys," he says. "Most of 'em were empty suits."

To this day, George has a knack for going to the tracks in style. As recently as the summer of 1969 George was back at Saratoga, quite comfortable in the home of Harry M. Stevens III, a young Stevens of the family that invented the hot dog, the straw, the paper cup and now caters no fewer than forty-one tracks and stadiums around the country. Sitting on young Harry's porch one evening, George was asked by his host if he wanted to pitch coins at a line for cash.

"Now what would I do with a catering business?" said George.

But let's retreat back to those 1930's again, to the days when Low honestly felt he could make it all the way from his assistant pro jobs into a handsome living on what had become a burgeoning PGA tour.

George started out on the tour determined to make his way as a champion, but, well, it was just too much fun in those days. Card games all through the nights—pitch and bridge, that kind of thing. And there were all of these characters to pal around with—Demaret, Jimmy Thomson, Leo Diegel, Craig Wood. "And that Indian," he says. Which was Ky Laffoon.

"Laffoon is the only man who ever beat me outa something on the putting green," says George. "At the old North and South Open at Pinehurst we got into a game that lasted day and night. I should have known I was in trouble when we putted at night. Laffoon was an Indian and Indians can see at night. I didn't get in that jackpot no more."

Low made an attempt which might generously be described as feeble to win the British Open of 1939. The idea of returning to semi-native soil gripped him, one reason being that he might be able to redeem himself for the last round he had played in Scotland. A long time before, in the

British Boys' championship at Edinburgh, George had been beaten 8–7 by a cross-handed Scot, and he was so disgusted about it he heaved his clubs out of a train window. So George and Johnny Bulla sailed on the *Transylvania* in the summer of '39 for England.

The trip abroad took too long for George. Struggling to occupy his time on board ship, he got into a high-stakes game of shuffleboard with a gentleman of nobility, and he lost so much money that he was forced to delay his arrival for the British Open. Instead of going straight to St. Andrews he went with the earl or count or whatever he was to Perthshire. There they would bowl on the green.

"My bankroll looked like an elephant slept on it when I got off the ship," George explains. "Took me three weeks bowling on the green to get it back."

Low finally got to St. Andrews but not in time for a practice round. And he isn't altogether clear on how well he played. "I think I missed the cut—if I teed off at all," he says. "I forget. In those days, me and Clayton Heafner had a bad habit of being withdrew."

Where are the characters on today's tour? That's one thing George would like to know. Where are the fun-lovers, the withdrews? "All you got out there is a bunch of authors and haberdashers," he says.

"All you got to do to write a book is win one tournament. All of a sudden you're telling everybody where the V's ought to point. And them that don't win, they're haberdashers. They sell sweaters and slacks and call themselves pros."

Says George, "There ain't many of 'em knows how to repair a club in a shop. They can bend 'em, but they can't work on 'em until they know what's right. Most of 'em couldn't win consistently if they had Dick Tracy for a partner. I do a little club work for a few of 'em, but there's not too many who'd give the ducks a drink if they owned Lake

Mead. They'll pop for a handshake, but those I got plenty of."

One of George's last flings as an active tour player came in 1945, and history confirms that he went out beautifully. Among the more remarkable facts of golf is that George Low helped end the fantastic winning streak of Byron Nelson. It happened in the Memphis Open that summer. Nelson, the Mechanical Man, had won eleven straight tournaments when he got to Memphis to try for the twelfth. Nelson finished third at Memphis behind Amateur Freddie Haas, who shot 270, and none other than George Low, who shot 276.

"Haas win the tournament, but I win the front money," says George. "I was the first pro to beat Nelson. Look it up."

Very shortly after that Low retired to the putting greens forever.

So many legends and half-truths have been written, spoken and whispered about George Low's putting ability, he ought to be a folk song. There are wild tales of George putting with a rake, a shovel, a pool cue and a broom handle and defeating others using a legitimate putter. There are stories of George kicking the ball with his foot and acing five out of nine holes in one round on the putting green. Other stories say that George has given putting "secrets" to Arnold Palmer, Bing Crosby, Willie Mays, all sorts of celebrities who turn up in his photo albums with their arms around his bulky shoulders. And there are stories that in the old days George took so much money away from tour winners on the putting greens that he should have been given a speeding ticket.

Low only forces a sly grin when the stories are put to him.

"They get started because I lived good," he says. "I spend $50,000 a year of somebody else's money, that's all."

Oh, there are a few things George could talk about if he

wanted to get himself in some kind of jackpot, as he says, but it isn't worth it. Sure, he can kick the ball with his foot and get it down in two from almost anywhere. For example, at Las Vegas a few years ago he was walking around in a practice session with Bo Wininger when Bo plopped a ball down on the 16th green at the Desert Inn and said, "Three cases of beer to two you can't get it down in two from here." The putt was seventy-five feet long. George called it, put his shoe to the ball and rolled it up within two inches of the cup. And George *can* beat you putting, even if he uses a wedge. "Don't ever try him," Byron Nelson has warned.

"I shall have to admit, in all modesty, that I'm probably the greatest putter who ever lived," says George. "At least I'll try anyone for a nominal fee."

There is a simple reason why George Low is the greatest putter who ever lived. "I've done more of it than anybody else," he says. "Back in Scotland, in Carnoustie, there was a thirty-six hole putting green right outside our house. I putted for three or four years, eight, ten, twelve hours a day, before I ever started playing golf. I've always been able to do things with my hands anyhow. Build things. I have feel in them. So I putted and putted before I ever played golf, and then I've done nothing but putt since I quit. I can beat anyone on the tour because they have to worry about getting to the green. I'm already there."

George is not keen about giving away his putting secrets—not for free, at least. But he can offer a little advice.

"Everybody has a different problem putting," he says. "The best thing you can have is a quick left wrist. That makes you take the clubhead back on the inside. Most of your weight ought to be on the left foot for good balance. Another important thing is to keep both thumbs squarely on the top of the grip for the right feel."

He goes on, "The feel of the club may be the most important thing of all. When you reach in your pocket for a coin the last thing that touches the coin is your thumb. You use it to roll out the coin. It's the most sensitive finger. That's why you grip the putter with both thumbs on top of the handle."

And on, "After you get the feel of the club the thing to do is be sure you get a good, solid rap on the ball when you hit it. And there's only one way to be sure of doing that. Take the club back on the inside, like opening a door, and then bring it forward. When you open a door you take it back slow. When you close the door, that's the way the putter should meet the ball."

And on, "The worst way for the beginner to putt is to jab at the ball. You'll see some of the pros jab at it, but it's their own method they've worked out, which they think is good for all of the bad greens they putt on. There are a couple of 'em that jab the putt on any kind of green. Billy Casper, for instance, and Bob Rosburg. They're pretty good putters, but there are exceptions to everything. Besides, they jab the same way every time, which is the real key to good putting. Consistency."

And finally, "That's why I'm gonna beat everybody. I'm gonna hit the ball the same way every time, and you're not. And if we putt long enough for the luck to scare off, I got to be the winner."

George Low might be a more mysterious figure than he is if it had not been for Arnold Palmer. When Palmer won his second Masters in 1960, Low's name burst into print as some sort of weird genius of the greens—and all because of a remark Arnold made to the press. That year Palmer sank dramatic putts for birdies on the last two greens to win, not only before the thousands in Augusta, but before millions more watching television. And later on, in an interview, when asked about those heroics, Palmer said, "The only thing I did on those putts was keep thinking what my old friend George Low always says: 'Keep your head down and don't move.'"

A short time after this Low's small but impressive notoriety resulted in an autograph-model putter, the George Low putter, a mallethead type with a marketing slogan that went "the putter with the built-in touch." It was made by a company called the Sportsman's Golf Corporation of Chicago. A few of the pros began using the Low putter, mainly Gary Player. And exactly one year later, back in Augusta again, Player, using the Low putter, won the Masters and George Low got even more publicity.

"But I was lucky," says George. "The putter started selling so well I got fired. It was a relief. With a lot of money in your pocket, it takes away the torment of where you're gonna sleep."

Along about this time another change took place in Low's career. A motel chain, Ramada Inn, hired him as a goodwill ambassador. His job was to follow the tour and guide as many pros as possible into Ramada Inns across the land. They gave him a Cadillac to drive—"the only Cadillac in the press lot"—and let him have free rooms in all of the Ramada Inns he could locate.

"It didn't feel right," he says. "I knew it wouldn't last. Something was missing. The daily challenge that I'd grown used to. The challenge of whether I'd be able to borrow Frank Stranahan's car and lose it to somebody in a coin flip or something. It got so bad for a while I almost bought a pair of shoes on my own."

That wouldn't have been right. George hadn't bought a pair of shoes in thirty years. He'd got them all from Foot Joy. "I been a test pilot for Foot Joy forever. I test their sixty-five-dollar alligator models to see if standing in them for long periods of time in a bar brings them any serious harm. What effect spilling beer has on them."

Rarely is George anything in appearance but the portrait of prosperity. Foot Joy shoes, a handsome plaid jacket that he got from Joe Jemsek, a golf course owner from the

Chicago area ("he wears my size") and a Western-tooled, monogrammed leather chair stool, courtesy of Bob Goldwater, Barry's brother.

"No if-come about him," says George. "Bob stands up."

There have been, sad to relate, times when George Low has insisted on paying up himself. Not often, but some. And only in these latter, more prosperous years. One such occasion was in Augusta in 1965 in a place called the Bull Bat Lounge, just off the lobby of the Town House Hotel. George was sitting with a few journalist friends he could trust, drinking beer and getting ready to go search for a cafeteria. He prefers cafeterias to elegant restaurants because they have a lot of vegetables. Anyhow, George was in the middle of an anecdote when an old friend appeared.

"Good to see you, Bubble," the voice said, the voice belonging to a Tampa car salesman named Madman Morris. "Where you been? I been all over. Pensacola. Miami. Everywhere. How come I didn't see you?"

"Madman," said George. "Either shut up or sit down and assume the financial obligation. I got my own lies to tell."

"Sure good to see you, Georgie," said Madman. "I know this guy thirty years. . . ."

"Are you gonna sit down and buy something, Madman, or just stand there looking like a buried lie in a bunker?" George said.

"I been all over, Bubble. Jacksonville. Pensacola. Miami. How come you wasn't anywhere?" Madman said.

"There's a rule in this joint that any guy stands around has to *buy* something," said Low. "Why don't you take your shag bag somewhere else and hit your shanks?"

"Whatta guy," said Madman Morris. "Same old George. I'd see this guy everywhere. Palm Beach. Orlando. Pensacola. Miami . . ."

"I can't get in no jackpot with an unplayable lie like this," said George, excusing himself, sliding out of the booth in the

Bull Bat Lounge, paying the check and leaving to go look for vegetables.

There are also occasions when George Low can be persuaded to play a round of golf. Actually play. Naturally, the type of golfing companion George prefers is someone with money and questionable talent, an ego-inspired handicap, perhaps. "Give me a millionaire with a bad backswing and I can have a very pleasant afternoon," George says.

An afternoon like this occurred not so many winters ago at the posh Seminole Golf Club in Palm Beach. George got into a game with the Duke of Windsor and the late Robert R. Young, the railroad magnate. An earl or a duke or a count could always entice George into a game of something. George's putter was good to him this day as it usually is when more than laughs are involved. The other shots he could hit well enough from memory. George came out in good shape, don't worry. Except that when the round was finished Low didn't notice the Duke straining to get in his pocket.

They were all sort of strolling toward the clubhouse—to the veranda, of course—slowly, amid a rather awkward silence. George cleared his throat a couple of times. They stopped and chatted about the nice day, how lovely the course looked this time of year. George shifted his weight from one Foot Joy to another and cleared his throat again.

Finally, Robert Young discreetly took George aside and whispered something to him.

"Oh, by the way, George. I should have mentioned that His Royal Highness never pays money," said Young.

"He don't do *what?*" said Low.

"His Royal Highness never pays. It's custom with him. It's rather a privilege, you see, to play golf in his company."

"Mr. Young," said George Low, the only George Low there ever was or ever will be in golf. "You take care of your railroads and I'll take care of my dukes."

The Tower of London

J. Bryan, III

What does the phrase "Tower of London" evoke? The headsman's axe and the torturer's rack, yes, but the background? Well, a big, grim, blocky building, buttressed and turreted, a sort of Henry VIII in stone. Yes, again; but the blocky building is only the Tower of London's black heart, though it is ironically called "the White Tower." The actual Tower of London, complete, is a complex of grounds and buildings that covers thirteen acres. Its formal title is the Royal Palace and Fortress of the Tower of London, but it is far more than that; it is a treasury, a garrison, two chapels, several armories and a museum. Until thirty years ago, it was also a prison; until a century ago, it was also the Royal Zoo and the Royal Mint; but foremost it was England's slaughterhouse, a national abattoir that ran with blood for 700 years.

Legends abound here. The most persistent is that the White Tower was built by Julius Caesar. Shakespeare makes his Richard II speak of "Julius Caesar's ill-erected Tower," and Thomas Gray supports him: "Ye towers of Julius, London's lasting shame." Not so. The builder was William the Conqueror. After his coronation in 1066, one of his first orders was for the construction of "three strongholds against the fickleness of the vast and fierce populace." Chief of the three was the White Tower. Since it would echo to such pain and grief, it was appropriate for its architect, Gundulf, Bishop of Rochester, to be known as "the Weeper." Gundulf was succeeded by another bishop, Rannulf Flambard of Durham, who so "pilled and shaved" the people for his building fund that he himself was thrown into the tower he had just completed—its first prisoner and, three years later, its first fugitive. Friends had smuggled him a coil of rope in a wine jar, and he slid 65 feet to the ground and escaped.

The tower the bishops built is roughly square, 118 feet by 107, and 90 feet high. Its stone walls are 15 feet thick at the base, tapering up to 11 feet. Parapets fence the roof, and a turret rounds off each corner. Later kings, notably Henry III (1216–72) and his successor, Edward I, girdled it with walls and a moat, and added ramparts and bastions, until it was one of the largest, stoutest fortresses in Europe. But the White Tower itself they left alone. Its exterior is just as it was 900 years ago, except for a coat of whitewash (hence its name) and for the windows that Sir Christopher Wren widened from the wary Normans' arrow slits. The interior, too, is just the same; thick walls divide each of the four floors into three rooms. The only difference is that the 20th century puts the rooms to uses different from those of the 11th.

Especially the dungeons. Once black and dank, they went 35 feet underground, and hungry rats swam through the gratings when the Thames was in flood. They have been filled in now to a depth of only 20 feet. Electric lights have been installed for the tourists, and wooden floors laid, and ancient cannon lie in rows there. But even if these dungeons were now sweet with flowers and music, old nightmares would still claw the walls. These are chambers of ineradicable horrors. Listen to Father John Gerard, imprisoned here in 1597 for the "crime" of being a Jesuit priest. The torturers put iron gauntlets on him and made him mount "two or three wicker steps," and fastened the gauntlets high over his head, then took away the steps, so that his whole weight hung from his wrists. Here are his own words: "The pain was so intense, I thought I could not possibly endure it. When I fell into a faint . . . they held my body up until I came to. Then they heard me pray and immediately let me down again. They did this every time I fainted—eight or nine times that day." His fortitude was such that, five months later, despite his crippled arms, he managed to escape.

The worst of the three dungeons was Little Ease, a four-foot cage, too cramped for a prisoner to stand upright or to lie. Guy Fawkes, of the Gunpowder Plot in 1605, was chained in Little Ease, kneeling, and force-fed on vinegar and mustard. He survived fifty-six days of it, but collapsed and confessed after thirty minutes on the rack. Confession availed him nothing. He and his fellow conspirators were hanged, cut down while still conscious, and disemboweled. The rack was broken up or hidden years ago; but "the Scavenger's Daughter," which crushed the body, is still on show, along with the bilboes, which squeezed the ankles; and the pilliwinks, which were a sort of thumbscrew.

Enough. Leave the dungeons. The first floor of the White Tower, originally quarters for the royal retinue, is now being restored. Leave this too and climb on, by the spiral staircase in one of the corner turrets. Notice that it spirals clockwise. If you were trying to storm it, your right arm—your sword—would be cramped, whereas the defender, above you, would be free to cut and thrust. As Gundulf knew, one nimble sword could hold this staircase against an army. On the second floor is the Chapel of St. John the Evangelist, two stories high, and the former banquet hall, now part of the armory. St. John's is the most beautiful Romanesque chapel in England, with its bare, cream-colored stone and high barrel vault. It is empty now, except for the altar and lectern. The murdered King Henry VI lay in state here in 1471; so did Henry VII's wife, Elizabeth of York, in 1503, her coffin surrounded by 800 candles; and in 1554, Mary Tudor married Philip II of Spain here, by proxy. The banquet hall, next door, served also as a prison—Charles of Orléans, captured at Agincourt, spent twenty-five years in it; and as a courtroom—Anne Boleyn was tried in it. Nothing is here now, but the weapons and costumes of ancient wars.

But such weapons! Such costumes! There is a shield that could "give fire" four times; and a combination spear, club, and three-barreled pistol; and an iron club with a spiked ball chained to it—its jocose nickname was "the holy-water sprinkler." There is a suit of armor for a horse, and one made for Charles II when he was five years old, and one for Henry VIII when his girth was 52 inches. Here, and in the armory on the floor above, are suits by the dozen, fluted and damasked, filigreed and arabesqued, engraved with royal devices and all of gray, gleaming steel.

The top floor was designed to be the royal residence and council chamber. All the early monarchs lived here and, down to James II, most spent their coronation eve here and returned after the ceremony for the coronation banquet on the floor below. Royal council chambers are seldom the scene of high drama, but this one was, in 1483. Richard, Duke of Gloucester, then Protector for his young nephew Edward V, strode into a meeting and demanded to know the proper penalty for a traitor. The boy king's chamberlain,

Lord William Hastings, said it was beheading, whereupon Richard shouted at him (so goes another legend),

Ere I dine,
I'll have thine!

and hammered the table with his fist. As if it were a signal, the guards seized Hastings and dragged him downstairs and outside to Tower Green. They did not bother to bring a block. They forced his neck onto a handy log and cut it through.

This is the moment to correct a popular misconception. There have been only seven beheadings in the Tower of London, all on Tower Green, and all the victims people of highest estate. The lesser rest—some fourscore—had to accept public execution outside the walls, on nearby Tower Hill. A prisoner arrived at the Tower either overland or by the river. Overland, a causeway across the moat delivered him to the outer ward. Entrance was through a gate in the Byward Tower (byward-byword-password), from which he was channeled along to the next tower, St. Thomas's (Thomas à Becket), where his path converged with that of prisoners arriving by the river entrance, the Traitor's Gate.

The Thames runs lower now, and the moat is dry; but in years past, the moat waters poured through this gate on an ebb tide with "so terrible a noise" that it was "enough to fright a prisoner out of the world before his execution." Sir Thomas More climbed the Traitor's Stairs; he was led ashore here in 1535, charged with treason for his refusal to acknowledge Henry VIII as supreme head of the Church. A year later, Anne Boleyn climbed them, Henry's second queen; and in 1542, his fifth queen, Catherine Howard; and on a wet day in March, 1554, his and Anne's daughter, Princess Elizabeth, soon to be a queen herself. Elizabeth had lingered in the rain, oblivious, to protest her loyalty: she was "a true subject, and before Thee, O God, I speak it!" God heard her; alone of the six, her climb up the Traitor's Stairs was not a rehearsal for the climb to the scaffold.

There are three other towers in the outer ward, making six in all. The inner ward has thirteen, of which four—Martin, Bloody, Bell and Beauchamp—are theaters where blood-boltered tragedies have played again and again. One of the stock questions that visitors put to the Tower's wardens, the Beefeaters, is "Which is the Bloody Tower?" The Beefeaters have a stock answer: "All of 'em!" One, the Martin Tower, is associated with blood of a special type: "Colonel" Thomas Blood, an Irish desperado. In the latter 17th century, such of the Crown Jewels and royal regalia as Cromwell had spared were kept in a ramshackle cupboard in the Martin Tower cellar, where the Keeper of the Jewels and his assistant, old Talbot Edwards, were allowed to exhibit them for a fee. One day in May, 1671, a white-bearded "clergyman"—Blood—having previously ingratiated himself with Edwards, returned with three accomplices and requested him to lead them to the cellar. As the old man did so, they struck him down. One robber grabbed the Black Prince's ruby and pouched it, and a second dropped the great gold orb into his baggy breeches, but two of the richest items were of awkward size: Blood had to stamp on a crown before he could handle it, and the fourth man was trying to file a scepter in two when the alarm was given and they had to flee. They got as far as the Byward Tower, a step from freedom, before they were seized. Try to believe what happened next: Blood, a common, merciless rogue, demanded a private audience with the King—*and the King granted it!* Not only that, but Charles II, ever unpredictable, forgave his crime and awarded him a pension of 500 pounds a year!

The jewels and regalia, along with the gold plate used at

state banquets, are now kept in the Jewel House. Guards and grilles and thick glass protect the treasure now, the great, glowing glittering heap of it, tier above tier. Above all the others, there is one jewel you must look for: the Black Prince's huge, glowering ruby—the same that Blood's men grabbed; and seeing it, you must think of what *it* has seen. From 1366, and the murder of its first owner, the King of Granada, through the Battle of Agincourt, where Henry V wore it in his helmet, down to poor old Edwards, enough blood has been spilled around this ruby for osmosis to stain it an even deeper red.

Archbishop John Fisher and Sir Thomas More are the more memorable alumni of the Bell Tower. Henry VIII clapped them there in 1535. Fisher was 76 years old, weak, ill, without shoes or clothing. When they came to lead him to Tower Hill, he begged for a cloak. The officer asked, "What need you be so careful of your health for this little time?" The old man explained that he did not want the crowd to see him shiver with cold and think him afraid. Two weeks later, his friend More, standing at the bottom step of the same scaffold, found courage to jest with the officer. "I pray thee, see me safely up," he said. "As for my coming down again, let me shift for myself."

If our admiration goes to these heroic churchmen, whole chords of our emotions are struck by the prisoners in the Bloody Tower: the Little Princes, in 1483; Bishops Cranmer, Ridley and Latimer, in 1555–6; Sir Walter Raleigh, in 1603–16 and again in 1618. There is no need to rehearse the smothering of the princes; that "tyrannous and bloody act" is too well known. In 1933, an examination disclosed that skeletons found in 1660 beneath the staircase in the White Tower belonged to boys aged about 13 and 9, that they had unusual and strongly similar facial characteristics, and that they had died of suffocation. Edward V was 13 years and 9 months old at the time of his murder, and his brother, Richard, Duke of York, was a few days short of his 10th birthday.

Raleigh—adventurer, poet, scientist, historian, gallant—was the Elizabethan Age incarnate; its flower, its plume, its pride. Elizabeth herself first sent him to the Tower, in 1592, for seducing one of her maids of honor, but freed him when he married the girl. Elizabeth died in 1603, and James I at once flung Raleigh back, as a sop to Spain. This time he stayed for thirteen years, writing his *Historie of the World,* drawing maps, making ship models, dabbling in chemistry and receiving the celebrities of Europe. Among them was the Prince of Wales. "Only my father," he said bitterly, "would keep such a bird in a cage!" James opened its door long enough to let Raleigh make one last expedition to South America. It failed, and he went back to the Tower, under sentence of death. On the scaffold, he felt the axe edge and remarked, "This is a sharp medicine, but it is a physician for all diseases." Then, as the headsman hesitated, "Strike, man! Strike!" He struck, and a voice groaned, "We have not another such head to be cut off!"

Last of all is the Beauchamp Tower. In 1552, it had the distinction of being host to the five Dudley brothers at the same time. The eldest, Robert, would become Earl of Leicester and Queen Elizabeth's favorite; the youngest, Lord Guildford, was the ill-fated consort of the ill-fated and still younger (she was only 17) Lady Jane Grey, next door. Anxiety had made her skin begin to peel and her hair to fall. She looked up from her Greek Testament one bleak day in February 1554, and saw her husband's headless body being carried back from Tower Hill. Her own turn was next. As Queen of England, even though for only nine days, she had the privilege of execution on Tower Green. Royalty also had another privilege; their executioners used a sword instead of an axe. Anne Boleyn established the precedent in 1536, when she sold her jewels to import a Frenchman, expert with the double-handed sword.

Five years passed before another condemned prisoner was held worthy of Tower Green. Again it was a woman: Margaret Pole, Countess of Salisbury, age 68, the last of the Plantagenets. She refused to kneel. "The block is for traitors!" she protested, and she dodged about the scaffold with her gray hair streaming and the headsman hacking at her until he hewed her down.

The next three victims were also women: two together in 1542: Queen Catherine Howard, and her confidante, Lady Rochford; then little Jane Grey, alone. The last of the seven was Elizabeth's discarded favorite, the rebel Robert Devereux, Earl of Essex, in 1601. In a final despairing plea for clemency, he sent her a ring she had given him, pledging her affection. It was intercepted, and the only favor he received was a scaffold on Tower Green instead of on Tower Hill. The headsman needed three chops. Happily, Tower Green needed no more headsmen. Folklore says that grass never grew where the scaffold had stood. No matter now; Queen Victoria paved the site and chained it off.

Something else she did at the Tower was to restore the little chapel at the corner of the Green, St. Peter ad Vincula, "St. Peter in Chains," where were buried some seventy-five high-ranking lords and ladies, most of them headless. Macaulay wrote, "There is no sadder spot on earth. Death there is associated . . . with . . . the savage triumph of implacable enemies. . . . Thither have been carried . . . without one mourner following, the bleeding relics of men who had been captains of armies, the leaders of parties, the oracles of senates, and the ornaments of courts." With the chapel floor collapsing above their unmarked graves, Queen Victoria ordered it taken up and relaid. Only thirty-three of the seventy-five skeletons could be positively identified, though one of the others was "almost conclusively" Anne Boleyn's.

("Almost?" She is known to have had six fingers on her left hand.) Known and unknown, all are at rest now.

More, much more, about the Tower deserves to be described: the Beefeaters, the Constable, the Ceremony of the Keys, the ravens, the ghosts (yes, well authenticated, too), but no space is left for it, no space and small inclination. We have had enough of man's inhumanity to man for today, enough of blood and anguish. Let a flippancy put them out of mind. Just across the moat is the Tower restaurant. We don't need a menu. Our order writes itself: a Bloody Mary (made with Beefeater) and a chop, well done.

Misconceptions
About the Human Mind

Ashley Montagu and Edward Darling

Mistaken ideas about our minds and how they work are no less widespread than those about our food and the bodies we inhabit, and in many instances it is less easy to present definitive proof in the area of psychology than in the other two. At any rate, we know a great deal more about the working of the human mind than we did a few decades ago. But one of the first ideas we should examine is the notion that certain mental states are "unnatural" or "abnormal." Deep in our hearts we suspect that when we use those terms we are not being entirely honest. To commit murder, for instance, we say is abnormal—it is an extreme deviation from ordinary conduct. And we are very eager to send the wife-killer to the electric chair or the gas chamber. Good enough for him! Yet how many of us are there who have never felt the *urge* to kill?

The very fact that a state or an action exists is proof that it is within the order of nature. Therefore "abnormal psychology" is fully as absurd a term as "abnormal physics." The ways of the "savage" are fully as *natural* as the ways of the Lord Mayor of London—and both have moments of being faintly ludicrous from the standpoint of the other man: the Lord Mayor insists on dressing for dinner, no matter how hot and uncomfortable the night may be; he chokes himself with linen and starch, instead of ripping off the silly shirt and letting the soft breezes cool his fevered skin. The "savage" laughs at this; yet if his own mother-in-law comes between him and the moon so that her shadow falls upon the food, he will not eat at all that night, because of his personal taboo. What the Lord Mayor does may be equally as ridiculous as the conduct of the savage; but neither is unnatural. "The unnatural," said Goethe, "that, too, is natural." Agreeing, George Bernard Shaw held that pretending that certain ways of thinking or acting are unnatural is a conspiracy to convict Creation of indecency. However, the type of mentality which Mencken used to characterize as the Philistine convicted Creation of indecency without a qualm; and so did Anthony Comstock—and lots of other people suffering from a burden of guilt which they could not admit to consciousness.

So it's agreed, is it, that we are talking only about natural phenomena?

THE MAN'S INSANE!

One quick look into the eyes of the fugitive, and the hawk-eyed detective realized that the poor creature was out of his mind. Any experienced operator can tell at a glance. Or at least that is the nonsense which is prevalent and thoroughly believed by thousands of readers. In this department nothing is less reassuring than to be confronted with a score of newspaper photographs and be required to rate the owners of the faces as villains or geniuses. Try it on your friends. The scowling rascal who has obviously just removed the dagger from between his teeth turns out to be the learned Bishop of Omaha; and the baby-faced choir singer turns out to be—guess who?

Actually, the "wild" look sometimes observed in the eyes of the insane is nothing but a superstition. Some insane persons do have a wild and furtive look; but so do some supposedly normal people. As a rule, mentally sick people look just like other persons.

THE FACE BETRAYS THE MAN?

"There's no art," says Duncan the King, "to find the mind's construction in the face. He was a gentleman on whom I built an absolute trust." And so he executed the Earl of Cawdor and gave his properties to Macbeth.

Yet our literature and our folklore are always reading character in the person's "wide, intelligent eyes," or in his "thin-lipped cruel mouth that turned down at the corners," or his "jutting chin that proclaimed the belligerency for which he was famous."

Any attempt to take the part for the whole, any simple rule-of-thumb interpretation of so complicated a matter as character, is folly. We don't even know why it is that we like certain faces at first sight or fear others. One case study was made of a child who bawled his head off upon the close approach of Santa Claus; and the fear was traced back to a shaggy dog who had upset the crib years before. The youngster had forgotten all about the incident and so had everybody else; but he had not forgotten the fear of furry things close to him. Thus the entire subject of personal love and distrust, of attraction and repulsion, can be extremely complicated and delicate.

Probably there is a correlation between character and appearance—but the connections are so minute and varied that no simple explanation can account for them. But we still seek the simple answer: a fat man is jolly; a long face is sad; blue eyes are honest; red hair means a hot temper; black men are lazy; Chinamen are inscrutable. We have to take short cuts to truth inevitably, but we should be aware of our probability of error. John Bull is not really England; Uncle Sam is not really the United States; Mlle. Fifi is not really France.

HERE WALKED HERCULES

Judging by the footprint, the old saw held, Hercules must have walked this way. And very possibly he did; but the footprint is only an indication and not a proof. To judge human character by the face alone or by the handwriting or the footprint is hazardous business and fraught with the possibility of error; yet we habitually judge the whole by a part of the whole, perhaps on the theory that we can never get to know the whole anyhow. Maybe we have to do it that way. All the more reason why we should be conscious of the incompleteness of our knowledge and avoid being absolute about an opinion which is necessarily based on less than total information. There have been theologians, as someone remarked, who have described the nature of God with a detailed assurance from which an experienced zoologist would shrink in explaining the genesis of a black beetle. But we do tend to accept judgments made on the basis of the footprint alone. *Caecorum in patria luscus imperat omnis* (In the land of the blind men a one-eyed person can be king of everything), as Fullonius was so fond of saying.

With this warning, we can now report that the colors which a woman selects for her personal attire provide a clue to her personality. Self-confident girls favor neutral grays and beiges, fewer warm colors, hues of medium value—not too dark, not too light. Those who are insecure pick brave, bright colors, plus extremes of very light and very dark cloth. So says research expert Beverly S. Cave after testing some Penn State coeds. The aura of nonsense attaches to these findings only if one accepts them as more than indicative possibilities—the part which *may* indicate the whole.

THERE ARE RECOGNIZABLE TYPES OF MEN?

The criminal, the saint, the greedy, the ambitious, the fearful, the courageous—these and other types of men can be spotted by the trained eye, according to the wisdom of the folk. And not of the folk alone but also of the academy. The late Professor Earnest Hooton of Harvard held that "criminals are physically differentiated according to the types of offense which they commit and they are biologically as inferior to humble but law-abiding citizens as they are sociologically."

Hooton popularized the subject of anthropology—even *Life* devoted occasional pages to his writings—and he was fun to read; but he could get as much mileage out of a skidding banana peel as the traffic would bear. In the citation just given he was dead wrong. Among those who specialize in these matters it is a favorite parlor game to line up photos of most-wanted criminals and mix them up with photos of most-respected clergymen and jurists, and then allow some

innocent at the party to select the vicious from the benefi-
cent. The results are often fantastic, and seldom accurate.
Maybe this means that at bottom all crooks are potentially
clergymen and jurists, and vice versa. We must investigate
that rich vein. Meanwhile beware hagiography, star readings,
and uncontrolled use of LSD.

LUNATICS — THE HAPPY ONES?

"How happy is the moron," sang Dorothy Parker, "he
doesn't give a damn!" In much of popular fiction the de-
mented are represented as enjoying their condition, sometimes to the point of actual bliss. "I am Napoleon, and it's
wonderful. Of course, I have a great many responsibilities,
but it's worth it." Was it not Dryden who wrote:

> There is a pleasure sure
> In being mad which none but madmen know.
> *The Spanish Friar,* Act II, sc. 1

In support of this popular fallacy, one must admit that in
the manic-depressive psychoses there are certainly manic
states of wild elation, and perhaps it is these, in part, which
are responsible for the generalization that lunatics are happy
in their illusions.

However, those who have worked with the mentally sick
know all too well that there is no state so bitterly tragic as
mental illness. The misery of the mentally disturbed is
beyond the conception of those who are unfamiliar with it.
Patients who have endured a severe mental disturbance and
have recovered thoroughly enough to be able to give a co-
herent account of their feelings while ill agree on one thing
—that the suffering is intense beyond all comparison with
anything else they ever knew.

CAN THE THINKER HAVE A TAIL?

If it was shocking, sinful, heretical, and just plain awful for Galileo to demonstrate that the earth is not the center of the universe, think how terrible it was for Darwin to demonstrate that man, far from being little lower than the angels, was in fact an animal himself, subject to the laws governing all animals. The favorite defense among those who had to admit Darwin's evidence was that, if man was an animal, at least he was the only rational animal: he was the only animal that could reason. The idea, despite the findings of Freud, lingers. It is one of the most tenacious among popular fallacies: only the tailless wonder can reason. Thus Daglish: "No beast has the power of reasoning out a course of action and of moulding its behavior on a preconceived plan."

We know better today, whether we like to dwell upon the subject or not. The minds of men and the minds of animals are alike; they differ only in degree. The evidence showing that the great apes solve many problems logically and reasonably is "abundant and convincing" to Yerkes. In his book *The Great Apes,* and in evidence supplied by investigators such as Köhler, Kohts, and numerous others the last doubts are removed.

One of the most convincing demonstrations—and most dramatic—was conducted by Dr. W. N. Kellogg, who for a period of nine months adopted a chimpanzee and brought him up along with his own year-old son. The chimp was, in fact, a few months younger than the boy. There was no question but that the young ape was temporarily more intelligent than the baby: he could remember better, understood more words, perceived more readily how to use tools, and was brighter in many ways. Toward the end of the period the human baby was beginning to outstrip the ape, as expected; but this doesn't mean that the chimpanzee did not continue to "reason" within the limits of his mental powers.

Indeed, any reader of Gertrude Lintz's accounts of her chimps, Joe and Maggie, can have little doubt of their intelligence. "Chimps," she says, "can put two and two together, which is all that thinking amounts to."

Confronted with such evidence, there are those who will still retain their conviction that only mankind can reason because man alone can laugh. But that bastion, too, has fallen. In both his books on apes Yerkes presents conclusive proof that these mammals do laugh. According to Yerkes, man's distinction is that he alone sheds tears, which is a dismal substitute indeed. Let him weep alone.

Despite anything said in this article and despite any proof adduced, we can have a warm assurance that most of mankind will continue to believe that our species alone can reason. Aristotle said so himself; and the Church. for twenty centuries taught that man alone has a soul, the ability to reason, and hence the freedom to make choices between good and evil from which moral responsibility derives. And, more than that, the human ego is fed so comfortingly by the conviction that only man is wise. No—we're not going to drop the idea; not this afternoon, anyhow. But for those who like to pile up illustrations in case of argument, consider the facts as set out by Loeser and innumerable other investigators, who have shown that every animal is capable of some degree of intelligence.

Spiders do not spin their webs from a single instinctual pattern: they adapt their work with consummate skill to the requirements of the particular location in which they are working.

Some spiders will use the web of another if possible, rather than go to the trouble of spinning their own. Even an old, dusty, abandoned web with the roof falling in, as it were, is sometimes preferable to all that spinning needed for a new pad.

If a spider is feeding on a captured fly and another fly zooms into the web, the spider will fasten down the first fly securely, grab the second and spin a net around it, and then return to the interrupted meal.

And some spiders, says Loeser, "which had lost one or more legs were seen to give up weaving webs and go hunting for food until their limbs had grown again."

Similarly, adaptations which bees make to an environment for which instinct could not have prepared them give the appearance of reasoning: ordinarily a honeybee goes about preparing the comb as a first order of business; but if offered a ready-made comb, it will skip that step, ignore its "building instinct," and immediately set about the business of hatching. Duplication of effort seems to offend its sense of orderly procedure. In the same way, if bees are given unlimited supplies of sugar, they abandon their "instinctual" storing away of honey for the off-season.

In the Loeser book oft-cited that scientist's observation is that there are no "instincts" in the old sense of the word in the entire animal kingdom: nothing that sets a whole pattern of behavior to work at a given signal. All animals, he thinks, are aware only of simple sensations and they respond to these as they occur. Most psychologists today maintain that this is even more true of man than it is of any other creature.

MAN'S MIND IS IN HIS BRAIN?

That argument need not detain us; we can observe the incredibly clever manner in which a hermit crab places a sea anemone on the shell of the mollusk in which he is making his home, and then we can call that action anything we like. If you cannot accept the proposition that animals are capable of thinking, you'll call this instinct. To others it will appear as intelligent action. As John Ray, the seventeenth-century English naturalist, wrote in his *Collection of English Proverbs* (1670), "Let him make use of his instinct who cannot make use of reason." Jennings concluded in 1906, after an exhaustive study of unicellular organisms, if they didn't think, they certainly behaved as if they did.

Hoary with age is the notion that the mind of man is a specific organ located in the head or the brain; nothing could be further from the truth—but one would never guess it from our language. Look up "lunatic" in a thesaurus and you find "softhead," "shallowpate," "saphead," "numskull," "dumbhead," "blockhead," "lunkhead," "fathead," "clodpate," "harebrain," "bats in the belfry," and scores more, all indicating the profound conviction that the human mind is up there in the attic for sure. In Shakespeare's day the brain was thought to have three "ventricles"; one for the imagination, one for the reason, and one for the memory. This is a rich field for folklore; but we must skip all that to establish some facts in the case.

We think with our whole bodies and not with the brain alone. This fact was really known long before psychosomatic medicine became a science, but not by the folk, most of whom still think the mind is in the brain.

What we call "mind" is the accumulation of the experiences which have come to us from every part of our bodies. Those experiences make their impressions upon the whole body, too; but the brain is the central organ which stores and serves to integrate one experience with all the others.

Another way of putting it is to say that "mind" is behavior; and it is the body as a whole that does the behaving, not just the brain encapsulated by the skull. The brain is the receiving and transmitting station, and a great and complicated mechanism it is—but it is dependent upon all of the rest of the body for what it receives, and it is beautifully and wonderfully integrated with every other part of the organism.

An isolated brain would be powerless to do anything, however. And so would a body without the central nervous system and the brain.

Kraines and Thetford illustrate what happens by using the brilliant analogy of the ballet: "Just as the rhythmic, smooth, and unbroken movement of the trained dancer seems to be a graceful undulating movement, but is in reality composed of innumerable small contractions of individual muscle fibres moving in such rapid succession as to 'appear' smooth, so the mind, seeming to make decisions and to solve problems with relative simplicity, is in reality merely reacting to stimuli in terms of patterns established by countless hitherto experienced pains, frustrations, and successes."

Indeed, moving a finger—that simple gesture—is as much a mental activity as it is a muscular one. Mind might well be defined, in fact, as an expression of the body. The brain acts as organizer or inhibitor so that traffic moves one way at a time; if it did not, there would very shortly be chaos and everything would come to a standstill—which is exactly what happens during an interval of indecision: when the brain is frozen, the body is frozen. In a word, the *mind* is frozen.

"NERVOUS BREAKDOWN" COMES FROM OVERWORKING THE BRAIN?

Somehow one has never heard of a "nervous breakdown" resulting from too much gardening or too much wood chopping—the overwork that caused the breakdown is always mental. And the term *nervous breakdown* covers everything from a tantrum to insanity; it is employed so often to cover up some disgrace that a person of sensitive social graces, once he hears that "Henry has had a nervous breakdown," pursues his questioning no further, lest skeletons be heard rattling in family closets.

The truth is that a nervous breakdown, whatever form it

may take, always has a long history of mental conflict or frustration behind it. The breakdown represents the crisis which has brought the whole conflict to a head. At this point the sufferer must find the solution to his problem—or withdraw from society in one way or another. Some manage it, others do not.

The people who are deemed to be in greatest danger of facing a nervous breakdown through overwork of the brain are the high-tension executives in business who are running the machinery too fast and without a rest; or the intellectuals, scholars, scientists too devoted to their labors to take an afternoon off at the ball park. It is commonly held that these people either wear out the brain tissues or cause them to be inflamed in some way.

There is not the slightest ground for such beliefs.

Any part of the body can suffer from fatigue, including brain cells; but brain cells cannot be fatigued by mental work; no amount of this is capable of exhausting the brain. No one ever uses more than a small fraction of the potential brain energy he possesses. But anxieties and bodily fatigue or illness can make sustained mental application difficult. Which is quite a different thing from saying that the condition is the *result* of the concentrated mental work. Stop worrying: you may overwork the body—it tires fairly easily. But you're not going to overwork that marvelous mechanism up where the gray begins.

The idea that the mind becomes tired from working is a popular fallacy derived from a false comparison with muscular work. The whole psychosomatic organism may become weary; but the brain itself is no more fatigued than is the conducting wire which carries electricity to your light bulb. Man, it has been variously estimated, is born with between 10 billion and 14 billion brain cells. It has also been estimated that from the age of 35, and often much earlier, we begin to lose between 10,000 and 50,000 of those brain cells a day. But don't worry, a simple arithmetic computation will show you that by the age of 70 you will still have at least 9 billion brain cells left.

DO YOU WALK IN YOUR SLEEP?

There is a most curious notion firmly established in the folkish mind that if you do happen to walk in your sleep there's nothing to worry about because you are perfectly safe—that is, you are in the hands of God, so to speak—as long as nothing suddenly wakes you up. As in the old flicker cliffhanger thrillers of Harold Lloyd's, you may walk out onto steel construction skeletons of skyscrapers, right along on one of the beams overhanging Madison Avenue a hundred stories below, reach the end of the beam and decide to turn around and come back—and end up safe and sound in your own bed. As long as you are walking in your sleep you're presumably safe. But if you should be awakened on that high steel beam you'd be subject to all the normal fears that flesh is heir to, and probably lose your balance in terror. The popular myth, incidentally, is usually not at all interested in sleepwalkers until they are on a ridgepole, a cornice, a high girder, or the edge of a cliff—at least the walker is envisioned in some very great peril to which, awake and in command of his faculties, he would by no means commit himself.

In discussing this particular popular fallacy we can only begin by pointing out that there are no recorded cases of persons sleepwalking themselves into situations of great peril. Into situations fraught with potential social embarrassment, yes—like walking into the crowded living room in one's pajamas. But onto high girders, no. Apparently the only real danger in suddenly awakening a sleepwalker —especially a child—is that the awakening confronts the

sleeper with a confusion between what he thought was going
on and what he now sees *is* going on which can mount to a
point where the walker cannot be sure which is real and
which dream. Prolonged confusion in this department could
invite powerful emotions which might be inhibitive or otherwise dangerous. None of this would be true in the case of
the awakened person who instantly saw his predicament and
recognized the real and the imaginary.

Seeking the origins of this very widespread belief that
sleepwalkers are immune to harm unless suddenly
awakened, we find ourselves pretty deep in primitive religion. We are dealing now with the wandering spirit—soul,
ghost, essence—which goes where the body cannot go and
remains after the body has died; the spirit that watches over
a man when his faculties are dormant; the little white
mouse-soul that comes out of a man's mouth when he is
asleep and actually does the things of which the sleeper
dreams (this is a German version; in another form of the
story the white mouse becomes a little bird). In most of these
old stories the central fear is that the soul may not rejoin the
body by the time the body awakes—and this would be very
bad; it might even cause the death of the sleeper. And right
there, perhaps, we have put our finger on the deep source
of the popular belief about sleepwalking.

Among many nonliterate peoples it is believed that it is
dangerous to wake a sleeper, because his soul is away and
may not return in time. If a sleeper *must* be awakened, it
should be done gradually so that the soul will have time to
return.

No human mystery is more common to people everywhere
than the adventures of a dream which seem to be as real as
any experience can be. The reader can undoubtedly recall
dream experiences of his own which were so real that the
ordinary ritual of rising, washing, dressing, and having
breakfast are all merely semireal until the spell wears off. It

would be interesting to determine whether there is any relationship here with the equally widespread fables of invisibility, where the protagonist, by virtue of some magic object, can go where he will without being seen. Usually the magic object is a cloak, a cap, a ring, a stone—although it can be something considerably more esoteric, such as a dragon's crown or the heart of an unborn child. Thompson's index lists twenty-eight such objects which render one invisible. The invisibility magic, in its turn, seems to be associated with other such excellent props as inexhaustible purses or pitchers, caps conferring wisdom, swords which cannot fail, rings and other objects which (compare Aladdin) summon spirits, and so on. Where is my wandering soul tonight?

IN A DREAM OF FALLING, IT IS FATAL TO HIT BOTTOM?

Since it is not possible to state surely what a person is dreaming about from watching him sleep, we would not be able to connect his dream with his death if he happened to die without waking. Hence the answer to the proposition that you will die if you hit bottom while dreaming of falling is one we cannot answer. However, we know that plenty of people have dreamed that they were falling, and wakened to fall again another night.

The psychoanalysts tell us that the dreams of falling are symbolic of personal anxieties, and this is not hard to believe—nor does it increase our knowledge very much. Freud attached an erotic significance to such dreams, as nobody will be surprised to hear. He says, "Nearly all children have fallen occasionally and then been picked up and fondled; if they fell out of bed at night, they were picked up by the nurse and taken into her bed."

The most we can say about this is that there is no evidence

that hitting bottom will cause death, since the only information we have is from those who did dream of falling, did hit the bottom, and lived to recount the horror of it all. If anybody wants to double his anxiety by thinking that he'll die if he hits bottom in this dream of falling, the thought is there for the taking.

HUMAN NATURE NEVER CHANGES?

"You can't change human nature." "It's only human nature." "Human nature is the same everywhere, always was, always will be." These are ideas which one hears expressed again and again. "What can you expect? It's only human nature." "Human nature will not change," said Abraham Lincoln. *Natural expellas furca, tamen usque recurret,* wrote Horace. "If you drive Nature out with a pitchfork, she will soon find a way back."

The truth is that because human nature is the most changeable thing in the world we are human. A baby is not born with human nature: he acquires it through learning. A child that was deprived of the humanizing process to which all children, with a few exceptions, are normally exposed, would not develop as a human being. Every child is born with the potentialities, the capacities for being human, but he does not become what we recognize as essentially human unless he has undergone the socializing process which makes him so. All of us are born with the capacity to speak, but none of us would ever have learned to speak unless we had been repeatedly exposed to speech. A human being *learns* to be a human being, and it is because of his two million and more years of such learning that he has acquired a genetic constitution which makes him the most educable creature in the world, and by the same token the most naturally capable of change.

The endowments of biological potentialities with which each child is born are, within broad limits, similar, but the manner of their development will depend upon the patterns prevailing in the particular culture to which they are made to conform. Man, as an acting functioning human being, is custom-made, tailored according to the prevailing pattern of the culture in which he learns to be a human being. Human nature is what a human being *does* by way of being human, and what he *does* may vary infinitely, as we "survey mankind from China to Peru."

The basic substrata of potentialities which make it possible for the child, under the appropriate socializing condition-ings, to develop as a human being do not remain stationary. They, too, change. Man has not ceased to evolve, and there is today every reason to believe that his potentialities for human behavior are as subject to evolutionary pressures as they ever were.

It will always be possible to pick up scattered kernels of evidence to support the nonsense that human nature is al-ways the same everywhere, if you call it evidence that Thucydides (died 400 B.C.) says that many things have hap-pened and always will as long as the nature of man remains the same—meaning that it will remain the same. Personally, we don't call that evidence at all; just because a famous Greek historian held that opinion does not make it a fact: the same historian thought the world was flat. With our im-mensely strong wish to believe what we want to, we tend to collect the evidence that supports our opinions and so very easily we tread blindly past those which contradict them; hence the apothegm of the folk that the devil can quote Scripture to his own ends.

MORE HUMAN NATURE THAT CHANGED . . .

The Jewish people during the Middle Ages were bitterly persecuted by Christians who blamed them for the death of Christ and honestly believed that to kill a Jew was to earn credits toward heaven. As a result, many jobs were not open to Jews, and they tended to band together in city ghettos. Thus over several hundred years the Jews gained the reputation of being naturally adapted to city life and to fiduciary concerns, particularly as moneylenders. Christians did not lend money, because they could not, by law, charge interest. Jews did lend money and charged fair rates of interest—for which again they were hated. But our point is that the Jews had the reputation of being city-bred people with a sharp eye for the handling of coin of the realm. Yet when they were given a chance to become agricultural, as in Israel, it was immediately clear that they could make the desert blossom at least as far as any other people. In short, Jews are no more bent toward mercantile pursuits by "nature" than they are toward husbandry.

Perhaps the most dramatic change in "human nature" is the change we have seen in Western civilization—and now throughout the world—in the status of women. Western woman, above the rank of peasant, was inferior in strength physically and intellectually. She was supposed to have a smaller brain than man, and so on and so forth. The past half century has seen this very same species—if you want to call her that—prove that it can do everything a man can do except become a father. To balance that sad inferiority, one might recall that men have not been bearing babies much lately either.

THE ONE THING THAT NEVER CHANGES IS HUMAN NATURE

Taken out of any specific context and allowed to stand as an absolute statement in its own right, the headline above is simple nonsense, and is so proved with great ease as follows:

1. Human nature apart from humanity does not exist. Agreed?

2. Human beings—humanity, that is—are known to change both individually and as groups: that is, as families, tribes, or nations.

  a. Illustrative examples are filled in here.

3. Q.E.D., human nature does change.

It so happens that we have with us a few handy instances to slip into 2-a, "illustrative examples," and we would like to assume that the reader would be pleased to have them.

Elizabethan England was one of the most musical nations in Europe; the people of Renaissance Britain loved to sing and dance and play instruments. In part this could have been overcompensation for the sad state into which music in England had been driven by the Civil Wars and the Reformation; and in part it was certainly due to the contributions of Huguenot refugees and Flemish weavers escaping from persecution. Psalm singing was a real rage, as W. Barclay Squire of the British Museum points out, citing the fact that "from 1560 to 1600 alone there appeared in England some ninety editions of metrical psalms with music."

Popular music outstripped the church music; there were itinerant "pipers and fiddlers" in every tavern; and all the great noble houses had their own resident musicians, both to perform and to teach. After the defeat of the Armada in

1588, national music in England burgeoned and the booksellers offered all kinds of music books. Shakespeare, of course, refers to singers, musicians, and the art of music in scores of passages.

Yet today when one is asked to name a musical people, how many will name the English? The socioeconomic interests of the English were strong enough to lead the national effort in another direction—and history awards this people a garland of success in world trade instead of in music. The nature of the English nation—this was our point—did change within relatively few years. With their decline as a world power, the English seem to have turned to music once more.

Perhaps the Japanese people display an even more dramatic example. Only a little time ago—little more than a hundred years—they held themselves in isolation from contact with the West and even refused trade with American ships. In fact, more than fifty attempts were made by this country to establish trade relations with Japan prior to 1854. American whalers wrecked in Japanese waters were brutally treated and ports were closed. Commodore Biddle, for instance, anchored in Edo Bay in 1846 but was refused any consideration. Perry's first visit elicited strong antiforeign responses and he was not able to get any agreement until his flotilla returned in February, 1854, when two ports were opened and America was named in the treaty as a most-favored nation. Even then Japan was not "open" to trade. The treaties were signed only by the shogun (called the *tai-kun* or *tycoon* by Westerners) and the people were powerfully antiforeigner in attitude. Murders of Westerners were not uncommon.

Today, as we all know, Japanese industry itself reaches out for world markets—one can get cheaper radios, tape recorders, binoculars, cameras, and all kinds of gadgets from the Japanese than can be made in the land of the free and the home of the brave. Technologically the Japanese are a different people entirely from the old days of the home factories specializing in ceramics and a few other specialties. Within a few generations they were able to change their old ways so completely that they have altogether lost some of their original traits along with the ability to produce certain exquisite objects of art, the best examples of which now reside in museums. They have Westernized their culture, adopting the vices of the West, alas, along with the material prosperity.

In short, human nature is what one makes of it. It would be possible to cite scores of other illustrations, from the statement attributed to the sage Saïd of Toledo in the eleventh century, that the races north of the Pyrenees "lack all sharpness of wit and penetration of intellect," back to the remarks of Galen in the second century, that the reason for the levity, excitability, and emotionalism of Negroes was due to a weakness of their brains, resulting in a weakness of intellect.

As for those who say that human nature never changes, perhaps they mean that there are certain generalizations which can be made of all living organisms more or less always, more or less everywhere—like the tendency to avoid painful experiences and to seek pleasurable ones (which is about as broad a generalization as you can get!). But that is rather a different thing from saying that human nature is constant. And of course one can always find exceptions: the masochist, for example, deliberately *seeks* pain; the martyr seeks death; the suicide woos the bullet. And what about the moth and the flame?

Or perhaps what these people are trying to say is that we live in an orderly universe where the laws of nature are dependable and that in this dependable universe there is no effect without its cause. But they would be closer to the truth to say that the very essence of all life is change itself.

THE HUMAN IQ IS A CONSTANT?

If it were really possible to construct a scale for every person which accurately reflected his biological age and his mental age in such a way as to show indisputably the extent to which his innate intelligence potential had been reached at any given point, that scale would indicate what we loosely call a person's IQ, his "intelligence quotient." We take a rough reading in that direction today by saying that a 10-year-old should have the following intellectual attainments, and this particular 10-year-old measures below or above that level and therefore has an IQ of 140 (well above his age expectation) or of 90 (somewhat below what is expected). But there are so many variations that the scale itself and the IQ figure are nothing but probabilities. Yet parents of a 140 IQ child preen themselves, and so would you and I.

That the intelligence quotient is an unchanging figure, the same at four that it will be at ten, is generally agreed in lay circles. But the fact is that there are dozens of factors which can and do change the IQ. For example, Professor T. R. Garth, in 1935, attempted to discover whether the score of American Indians rated about 80 IQ could be modified if their children were placed in white homes in a white environment. In a very short time Garth found that the children in white homes obtained an average score of 102, while the brothers and sisters of these children who remained in the Indian environment obtained an average score of only 87.5.

Even more striking is Rohrer's report on the Osage Indians of Oklahoma. As a consequence of the discovery of oil upon their reservation the Osage were able to improve their living conditions substantially. On one test, the Goodenough "Draw-a-Man" test, the Osage children obtained an average score of 104 while the white children's score was 103. On a test which made use of language the Osage children made an average score of 100 while the white children scored an average of 98.

Actually, the idea that the IQ cannot change is cognate with the notion that human nature is always the same; and that old notion is allied to the belief that "you can't improve nature," a belief dear to certain granite-headed village prophets who want things done as grandfather did them and not otherwise. The first troglodyte who managed to build a fire in a cave was improving on nature.

What the IQ in fact measures is for the most part socioeconomic, emotional, and schooling experience, and very little else.

Back to the IQ: It has been shown that a child whose tests show him to have a low intelligence quotient is quite capable of raising that score if he is exposed to stimulating, pleasurable schooling early enough in life. Further, the investigations carried out on monozygotic twins separated in childhood and reared apart, as conducted by Professor Newman at the University of Chicago and by others, show that education and environment can indeed produce appreciable changes in IQ.

In short, human nature can be changed; IQ can be changed; and even animal nature can be changed, as witness the beloved axolotl: here is a little creature six to eight inches long, resembling a tadpole. He has external gills. If he is left in water, he stays an axolotl. But if the water is allowed to evaporate slowly, the animal loses his gills and fins, develops eyelids, and leaves the water to become a salamander. Thereafter his nature is not axolotlish but salamandrine. Any questions?

WHERE IS MY WANDERING MIND TONIGHT?

We have already pointed out that mind and body are one and not two, but the myth of duality dies hard. Probably this is natural enough; a dreaming man may be out on the mountain hunting the roan deer while his body lies quiet on his bed—and when he tells his experience of the dream, those who were near him all night may assure him with oaths that they saw him on his bed: he knows where he was. He was out on the mountain. The only explanation must be that the soul goes wandering. Yes, to be sure: he was abroad mentally, but at home physically.

For thousands of years mankind has been assured of its double nature, mental and physical, mind and body, spirit and flesh. Indeed, the Gnostics of the first century believed that everything was spirit, that what we see as physical is merely an aspect of spirit—it just *looks* or *seems* to be material. The mystery cults were imbued with this idea, and some religious views still teach the same thing.

This is a reflection of a human characteristic which it is hard to call by any other name than stupidity: while nothing is more important to us than the functioning, use, and health of our own organisms, our own body-and-mind totalities, we actually know less about them than we do about most things. We are close to complete ignorance—but that does not bother us, because we have our totemic, traditional, rich supply of nonsense to substitute for knowledge. Superstition can be much more credible than fact. If you say that the body is evil and the spirit is good, who is going to dispute you? All the godly know it's true. Lechery, greed, envy, pride, cruelty, selfishness—are these not sins of the body? So that the pure and conscious mind must drag the body before the spiritual magistrate, shaman, priest, or worse still, before the tribunal of the human judgment, to be punished. One recalls that Jurgen, visiting his father in hell, found the old gentleman complaining bitterly because the attendant devils were too lazy to torture him as much as he thought they should; and when Jurgen advised him to leave well enough alone, the old man cried out, "But my conscience, Jurgen!"

And so it occurs that, despite the plethora of articles in the mass media on the subject of mental and physical health, we continue on our way without learning very much. It is possible that the reason for this is that there are hundreds of ways in which we can avoid facts, but no way in which we can avoid the need for self-esteem: we must think well of ourselves. Hence if a fact comes up against a myth, a stupidity, an error, or a piece of nonsense, and if the fact tends to make one look less admirable than one likes while the myth allows one to retain the rose-colored spectacles, one will choose—guess what!

Aside from that consideration, errors about the human body are accepted on the basis of very little evidence, on none, on hearsay.

Further, there is a magic in language which, for everyone but those persons who have been trained to be critical—that is, trained to seek for alternatives before coming to a conclusion—seems to establish as fact almost anything that is *stated* as fact. If you drink sea water you'll go crazy—did you know that? No, it never occurred to me; but you must be right because the Ancient Mariner and heaven knows how many other sea tales of shipwreck and open boats all indicate the same thing. So it must be true. Yes, sir—drinking sea water drives men mad. . . . We are not saying, mind you, that drinking *enough* sea water *under certain conditions* will not increase the irritation caused by a lack of fresh water and perhaps increase the torture of thirst to the point where the brain goes foggy—possibly even to the point of insanity. But your correspondents have themselves drunk sea water . . . . We will quickly deny the corollary allegation which we can plainly see coming to the reader's lips.

Statements made by persons of authority are naturals for public credence. Even if the person making the statement happens to be an authority in mathematics and not in anything else, he can make headlines by condemning this or that act of the government, as we have seen so frequently in our own time. Several times the American people have elected a man to head the nation merely because he had been a famous military leader.

And of course fifty million Frenchmen can't be wrong: if enough people say it, it must be true. This characteristic of our species is behind the satire in Kipling's jungle story of Mowgli's being captured by the great apes. "We are great, we are free, we are wonderful. We all say so, and so it must be true," they chanted to him. Fortunately Mowgli was able to see an alternative—to wit, that they were wish-thinking, herd-minded, and basically pretty thick behind the ears. Perhaps Kipling had somebody else in mind besides the Bandar-log.

SOUND BODY A MUST FOR A SOUND MIND?

The old classical idea, *mens sana in corpore sano,* simply meant that a supreme good, for which everybody should make the old college try, was a healthy mind in a healthy body. It still is an unspeakably wistful ideal, and it is impossible to imagine anyone not wanting to achieve it, just as it is a wee touch doubtful that anybody ever does. But ideals are to aim at. That's an editorial comment.

The motto has somehow become distorted, perhaps largely by the physical culturists, who are in a position to judge only the second half: the sound body part. That emphasis has tended to spread abroad the conceit that a sound mind can exist *only* in a sound body—which is nonsense taken right out of the mother lode, pure and unadulterated. Darwin had a dyspepsia which made it often impossible for him to work for more than four hours a day. Thomas Henry Huxley suffered from severe gastric troubles, and so did Herbert Spencer. John Keats did some of his best work when his lungs were being eaten away by t.b., and so did D. H. Lawrence. Steinmetz, the wizard of electricity, the first man to make artificial lightning, had an irremediable deformity of the spinal column. And Freud for half his life had cancer of the jaw and larynx. Milton wrote when he was sightless; Beethoven composed magnificent works when he was deaf. You could load a hay wagon with examples if you could find a hay wagon.

Of course a disease which attacks the central nervous system can make a difference; but no parent should get the idea that having the tonsils removed is going to improve the mental capacity of a child. It may possibly take the child's mind off his discomfort so that the mental apparatus can *work* better. But a very much twisted and unhealthy body can be governed by a fine, unspoiled brain. Not that it always *is*.

SOUND MIND, SOUND BODY —SECOND STANZA

Having just gone to some trouble to prove that a perfectly functioning cerebral cortex can exist in a twisted body, it is perhaps only fair to the Greeks to say that the ideal still holds: a healthy mind has a much better chance in a healthy body; or, more strictly, it is much more likely that a healthy mind will be found in a healthy body than in a twisted and diseased one. We are now thinking, of course, of the findings of psychosomatic medicine in which the word *mind* means something a great deal wider than brain.

No reader of these pages, surely, has not experienced the debilitating effects of the extreme, muggy hot weather on the thinking apparatus. You know that you can "think" better in a cool place. You wouldn't want to take a final exam in a sticky, dripping-hot room with no air conditioning. Industry found this out long ago. Much as they love their workers, the big corporations would not have made life so much more comfortable for them—at enormous expense—if it did not pay off in terms of production. Let us not be naïve.

Further, the keen mind can be in part shaped by the hurt body: it is a question whether the savage satire of *Gulliver* would have occurred to the mind of Jonathan Swift if he had not suffered from what is now thought to be labyrinthine vertigo which first made him partially deaf and later probably drove him insane. That this proud and bitter genius died insane is history. The sharp mind, first affected by the unhappy body, finally lost its hold.

If the Greeks had said "a healthy cerebral cortex in a healthy body," the issues would have been more clearly drawn. Funny one of them didn't think of it.

CERTAIN DISCIPLINES "STRENGTHEN" THE MIND?

In the old dichotomy mind and body, thought of as being totally apart and different, like the spiritual and the physical, Psyche and Eros, it was no trouble at all to have a thought picture of the mind structured somehow with muscles which grow stronger the more they are exercised. Now of course if one practices a great deal with the discus, a particular set of muscles becomes more powerful; and those same muscles can be called upon for throwing a javelin or a rock or a rotten apple. The transfer of power to the javelin from the discus is close to total.

Therefore, by analogy, a study of geometry should increase the "muscles" of the brain so that they can handle problems of logic in general: you become successful at solving geometric problems, and as a result you are able to handle the problems of state in later life. Train a child to become a good chess player, and he'll turn out to be methodical, well organized, and keep his closet clean and his room picked up.

That's the theory. Plato suggested subjects that were good

exercise for the mind and kept it in trim, like an athlete in training. Even as recently as Woodrow Wilson it was conceded that studying Latin and math was great stuff for mind training: "The mind takes fiber, facility, strength, adaptability, certainty of touch from handling them," he asserted in a 1902 article. In short, there is a transfer of the ability to handle Latin over to the ability to handle problems in general, like the transfer of the discus thrower's muscles to spear throwing.

The theory was forced to surrender to facts when Thorndike and Woodworth began their researches in the psychology of learning; and now we know that a mind disciplined to solve problems in algebra may become expert in solving problems in algebra; but very little of that skill will be transferred to solving problems in other fields. The training in math may instill a love of exactitude and orderly procedure—these attitudes are the concomitants of learning; but a lawyer's skill in presenting a good defense owes practically nothing to his earlier training in math or Latin: it developed out of presenting legal defenses—which will not help him one whit in his golf score.

"Experiments on transference ranged, during the first twenty years of the century, through all psychological fields—memory, skill, judgment, thinking and reasoning. In all the amount of transfer found was amazingly small—quite insufficient to justify educationally the attempt to train a habit in any field other than that in which it is most required."

All this, of course, caused a revolution in American education: one studies the classics to become versed in the classics; Latin to become able to read Latin; math to do mathematical calculations—but *not* the classics because it's good for the mind or Latin because it develops fiber or math because it disciplines the brain to be exact. And of course the college entrance requirements have reflected this new understand-

ing. In 1900–1920 one had to have Latin to enter any Ivy
League college, to select only one of the changes.

You can train the mind, the brain, the cerebral cortex: but
you can't build muscle into it: you can't "strengthen" it.
Neither can you tire it out. So feel perfectly free to use it
any time you want to.

MAKING WHOOPEE RESTS THE MIND?

Some people make whoopee by running and dancing or
playing a mad set of tennis or doing some physical act that
uses up a lot of bodily energy; others, by going out on the
town and painting it red—and perhaps getting soused in the
process. Anything extravagant. And they justify the ex-
travagance on the basis of the popular nonsense that putting
the body to great exertion automatically gives the mind a
rest. It is true that much of the whoopee-making gives the
thinking apparatus a *vacation;* but since it wasn't the cerebral
cortex that was tired in the first place, violent physical activity is no "rest" for the brain.

Now, this is not to say that mental fatigue, so called, cannot occur. It can, just as an electric motor can burn up its oil
and finally stick; but the copper wire leading electricity into
the motor did not wear out, tire, or run short of oil. The
wire will carry electricity in proper amounts for ages. And
the cerebral cortex is like that copper wire: it does not tire or
clog. What does get fatigued is the whole organism: and
since body and mind are one, we say the mind is tired.

Idleness, sleep, lolling on the beach, or playing a hot game
of tiddlywinks would give the "mind" as much rest as anything. What's required is a change, a holiday from the mental activity that has engaged the whole organism. Perhaps
you'd rather scream and shout and jump up and down; in
that case, by all means do so—but don't strain yourself.

DO INTELLIGENCE TESTS
TEST INTELLIGENCE?

The word *intelligence* is derived from the Latin *legere,* to perceive, and *inter,* between or among. According to Webster, it means, first, the power of understanding; second, the "power of meeting any situation, esp. a novel situation, successfully." In other words, it is the perception of alternatives. If the organism is confronted by a problem situation—such as being trapped behind a wire fence or cage with the only opening at the top—and it tries to force its way out by going straight ahead into the wire, time after time, without seeing any alternative way of attempting escape, that organism is less intelligent than the one which, after a few trials, looks around for another way, such as up. The lobster in a fisherman's trap remains, and is finally eaten, because he does not try enough alternatives. He is not locked in there: a way out exists. But not for an organism of his intelligence. Fortunately for lobster lovers.

The ability to discern alternatives is one which can be learned. If one's experiences within the environment are strictly limited, intelligence naturally does not grow as it would under richer surroundings. That was given as one excellent reason why the Nazi soldier was inferior to the American soldier when both were thrown into unforeseen circumstances: one had learned to obey unquestioningly; the other had been trained to act independently and imaginatively until the time of his induction; and those early years counted in terms of intelligence: the Yank saw alternatives.

But the so-called "intelligence tests" do not measure intelligence. They measure an expression of socioeconomic, cultural, and schooling experiences, and very little else. If they come anywhere near measuring the genetic contribution to intelligence, it is at a considerable distance removed.

IQ tests have their uses in telling us where a child stands at his age level in relation to other children of the same age level, in terms of the performance arbitrarily established by the tests themselves. Used as an administrator's tool for placing children in more or less homogeneous classes in a school, they may have their place —although the whole question of homogeneous classes in a democracy is still moot. The tests at least will be reasonably accurate in separating the efficient readers from the inferior readers, if that's the way you want to group children in a school.

From another point of view, however, these famous tests have done more harm than good, operating as a tyranny determining the teacher's attitude toward an individual child. If little Willie is shown to have an IQ of only 90, then is it not foreordained that his performance will be inferior? So why bother with him?

Actually, the low IQ child may have intelligence far superior to that of a child ranking high on the tests. Perhaps he simply lacked the environmental conditions necessary to develop his full capacities, since intelligence is learned. A low score is no more a test of the quality of intelligence than a high score is an indication of genius; and the injustices committed against low scorers in our schools often have grave consequences, especially for the underprivileged. We know that when the environment improves the scores on the tests improve.

The Friend

Robert Murphy

The loons had built their nest within five feet of the water on a lonely lake in eastern Canada's Laurentian Shield country, for they loved solitude and for three summers had found it there. No one but a rare Indian looking for good fishing ever wandered that way. The soil had been scraped thin by prehistoric glaciers. The land was remote, stony and infertile. A few white birches grew among the somber pines and spruces, and cast their pale reflections on the dark, clear water near shore.

It was a land of brooding silence, a silence seldom broken except when the loons, one on the nest and the other fishing out on the lake, called to each other in their far-crying, weird, laughing voices.

They took turns brooding the two eggs, which would have chilled if they had been left for very long, and it was the female that was on them the morning the baby loon hatched. He would be the only one, for the other egg was infertile. After struggling to get out of the shell, he dozed and rested for a time under his mother's warm feathers, a small creature covered with soft, thick, dark down. One day he would be two feet long and weigh 15 pounds, one of the largest and most powerful of the water birds.

The old loon felt the stirring of life beneath her and raised herself a little to give it room; presently she stood up, looked down at the little one, and gave several soft, cooing notes to welcome it. She picked up the pieces of broken shell with her long, sharp bill, dropped them over the side of the nest, and carefully settled herself over the baby so that her warmth would comfort and dry it, then raised her voice to her mate out on the lake. Her wild yodeling call reached far over the water and perhaps told him her tidings, for he answered and turned toward shore. The young one, hearing the voice of his race for the first time, thrust his head out of his mother's breast feathers and surveyed his world.

A fox working the shoreline stopped a few yards away and looked wistfully at them. He was hungry, but only the last throes of starvation would drive him to dare the old loon's deadly, chisel-like bill. She looked menacingly at him, and the fox made a wide detour and went on.

Before the day was out the young loon was fed some small fish, instinctively swallowing them headfirst so that their fins wouldn't stick in his throat, and the next morning the old ones led him to the water. Loons are clumsy on land, overbalanced when trying to walk because their legs are set very far back for swimming and diving; they scramble ungracefully along, falling on their breasts every few yards, and the young one had trouble getting out of the nest and following them. He fell all over himself, and finally solved the problem of covering the short distance to the lake with froglike hops.

Once in the water, however, he was in his true element, for which uncounted generations of splendid swimmers had prepared him. Buoyant as a cork, he paddled happily about and made small dives as instinctively as he had swallowed the small fish headfirst, and when he tired, he climbed up on his mother's back and rode for a time. His down shed water as well as feathers would have done; he merely had to shake himself to be dry.

In the days that followed he grew rapidly and became so fat from his parent's good feeding that he was even clumsier on land than at first. Now he seldom went ashore. His diving improved, and feathers began to push through the down that covered him. As he grew more accustomed to the underwater world, it became an ever greater pleasure to him with its variety, its shadowy corners, and the larval insect life of the bottom. The periods that he left his mother grew longer. Now he went on short excursions of his own to explore this ever-changing subsurface landscape or the rocky shoreline. He began to catch the insect larvae and nibble on the underwater plants, and presently he was darting in among the minnows in the shallow little bays and pursuing them into their hiding places among crevices in the rocks. All the while his mother swam about or made long dives a little farther out, but kept an eye on him, ready to warn or join him if any dangerous creature appeared on shore.

One day they were well down the lake, near a portion of the shoreline where they had never been before, and, as the young loon swam in close, a mink appeared among the rocks. Sinuous and dark, bounding quickly about, it leaped to the top of a lichened rock and paused with one forefoot raised when it saw him. It was a deadly little animal, strong enough to kill him and quite at home in the water, but the young loon didn't know that; he wasn't afraid of it but curious and completely unsuspicious. He swam in closer to it, and the mink leaped off the rock at him.

This frightened him, and he whirled about and dived, swimming frantically for deeper water, for loons prefer to escape danger by diving. But the mink was also a fine swimmer, and it might have gone hard with him if his mother hadn't surfaced from a dive in time to see the mink's leap. Running across the surface with beating wings, she came in like a racing speedboat in a cloud of spray and stabbed at the mink, but missed him in the flurry of water. Desperate fighter though he was, the mink decided not to face her, and slipped away around a rock and made his way ashore, vanishing into the underbrush.

The old loon swam about looking for the mink for a time, but finally gave up the search. Taking the young one with her, she moved out toward the middle of the lake. The young one stayed closer to her that day; he had had his first scare, and learned that it was better to keep a safe distance between himself and other creatures about which he knew nothing. He would always be curious, for loons as a race are full of curiosity. But the next time he would be more careful; the lesson wasn't lost on him.

When evening came and shadows grew long across the lonely lake, the old male, who usually fished much farther away, flew in to land with a great splash and a long slide across the water. Like all loons, he had comparatively small wings, and flew rapidly and with great momentum, landed fast, and needed a good deal of room. They all gabbled softly for a time together before going to sleep, and if one of them waked during the night, its laughing call would echo across the dark water.

When the mornings dawned clear and the sun rose above the hills to the east, the old birds, in their well-being and pleasure in life and the new day, would face it and give it welcome by standing almost upright on the surface with strongly flapping wings. The young one would do his best to imitate them, and, when the ceremony was over, the old male would leave them, running across the water with beating wings until he was airborne, and head for the other end of the lake.

The long days of summer were good ones for the young loon. As he grew to full size and gained in strength and skill in diving and catching fish for himself, he was more free to explore the underwater world that reached off into dim, mysterious shadows and pursue the creatures that lived in it. Now he was often left alone; his wing quills weren't sufficiently developed for flight as yet, and, although he wanted to join his parents in the air when they took off, he couldn't do it. He would run flapping over the surface with them and be disconsolate when they were airborne, but his dejection didn't last very long; the world beneath the surface was too interesting to him.

As he moved about, fishing for himself by now, waiting for his wings to finish developing, he gradually came to know the other creatures that shared his world with him: the bald eagle that sometimes soared above the lake, the ducks and mergansers that dropped in, the deer and moose and an occasional bear and other animals that came to drink or hunt around the shore. Sometimes he would approach the ducks and swim with them for a time, but, remembering the mink, he watched the other animals from a distance. They were all interesting to him, but the most exciting thing was an airplane that appeared above the lake early one afternoon, circled several times, and landed on the water in a cloud of spray. It was large and noisy, a mysterious visitor from another world; its engine shattered the silence as it skimmed over the water. The young loon dived and swam off, and when he came up again the plane was moving toward shore, where it became quiet and still.

The two old loons flew in from the other end of the lake and joined the young one, for they were very curious about this strange thing, and after gabbling together they moved in closer, swimming cautiously in circles and ready to dive at once if the plane made any threatening gestures. They saw a man get out of it and launch the canoe that had been tied down on one of the pontoons; another man and a boy then got out of the plane and into the canoe, and they all went ashore.

After walking around a little the people got into the canoe again and moved out on the lake, and began to fish.

The loons withdrew to a safe distance, and watched them.

One man was the boy's father; the other man was a guide, who had flown them in to fish for a day or two. It was the boy's first real fishing trip with his father, so much different from the short trips for the day that they made much nearer home in New Jersey, and much more exciting. The small plane flew so much lower than the two or three airline planes that he had been in that he felt he was exploring the increasingly lonely country rather than seeing it spread out miles below like a map. And when they landed on the lake, so remote from any evidence of civilization, it seemed that possibly no one had ever been there before.

The boy was thrilled to walk around a little on the shore and know they would camp there for the night; he felt like some of the explorers he had read about. They decided where they would pitch their tent later, and started fishing, and he had never seen such fishing. The trout were big and full of fight, and there were a great many of them; they kept a few for their supper and released the rest. The boy could see the loons swimming about and diving in the distance, and occasionally paused in his fishing to watch them, for they gave life to the quiet lake. Finally he asked the guide what they were.

"They're loons, big strong birds. Best divers in the world, I reckon," the guide said. "They dive and catch fish. They can even catch trout."

"Why are they called loons?" the boy asked. Are they crazy? I've heard crazy people called looneys."

"They sound a little like crazy people when they call," the guide said. "Maybe tonight they'll do it, and you can hear them."

The boy hoped he would be able to, and toward the end of the afternoon they went ashore again, got their gear out of the plane, made camp, and cooked their supper. By the time they had finished, the sun was setting behind the hills across the lake. The light wind that had been blowing all day dropped, and in the gathering darkness the lake became still as a mirror, reflecting the pale colors of the after-glow before it darkened to show the reflections of the stars.

Sitting quietly by the fire, surrounded by the vast primitive silence and the great primitive country about him, the boy imagined what it would be like to be alone, and longed to hear the loon voices described by the guide. A log in the fire broke in half in a shower of sparks, and then a loon's voice came across the silent night. It rose and fell eerily, and was indeed somewhat like crazy laughter, but it was more than that; it was a token of life in that lonely land that made it seem less lonely and remote, and somehow more friendly.

The boy would never forget the first time he had heard that weird and comforting call, and there was a warm place in his heart for loons thereafter. He would look them up in his bird guide when he got home. When next he encountered one of them, in far different circumstances, he would have no way of knowing that chance had brought him together again with one of the loons of his first fishing trip.

The days grew shorter and the nights chillier. Birds that migrated early could be seen along the shores of the lake as they moved toward the south. The young loon, after much trying, had finally got into the air. There had been considerable excitement the day he took his first amateurish flight. The old pair called repeatedly and flew around with him; they were joined by another pair and their two young, which had been flying past and were attracted by the calling, and all of them were very noisy and active in celebration until the late afternoon, when the visitors left and flew back to their own lake.

Now that he was airborne and soon flying well, the young loon was free to enjoy the pleasures of flight as well as the pleasure he took in the underwater world; no longer was he left behind, confined to the relatively small area he could reach by swimming. He was grown up now, he and his parents were equals, and he could go off on his own or join the others, and, for a time, this brought them closer together. Full of vitality from the summer's good feeding, they often played together. While they were frequently separated during the day, they seldom were very far apart at night, and on many mornings, before sunrise, the old male would call them together for a little diversion. They would gather, and, after sporting around each other, would fall into line, lift their wings, and, still in line, would take off on an amazingly swift footrace across the water. With their feet pumping rapidly and their wings half-extended, they would run for a quarter of a mile or so, wheel in a little half-circle, and race back to the starting point. The race would be repeated over and over, and then, as if at a signal, it would cease and they would gabble and call in their pleasure and exhilaration, and separate for the day.

As the days went by, the waves of migrating birds increased; there were more of them along the shore, and more ducks and several flocks of geese stopped at the lake. For a little while the mellow voices of the geese were added to the wild yodeling laughter of the loons. The young loon grew restless, for the mysterious urge to migrate—which he would do about three weeks before his parents—was growing strong within him. He flew about more. Circling high into the air, he would straighten away and head for another lake at 60 miles an hour, his big feet thrust out behind his heavy streamlined body and acting as a rudder.

At first this calmed his restlessness, but presently the urge for the south grew so insistent that one morning he circled up, pointed his bill south, and was on his way. He hadn't migrated before, and no older bird would show him the path or destination, but he didn't hesitate: an instinct handed down to him by his parents, still not understood by clever men, guided him. He fed and slept on the lakes of the Laurentian Shield, and when he came to the valley of the St. Lawrence River, the country changed to one more favorable for the affairs of men; farms and villages and highways and ships on the great river took the place of the lonely country where he had first seen the light of day, and long plumes of smoke crawled across the land above the bright and ephemeral colors of autumn. He couldn't know that much of this held danger for him, but his racial love of quiet and solitude held him away from it and saved him from danger or death.

He had never seen such a great expanse of water, and at first was rather lost and hungry in it, but he soon learned that the fishing was better in the quiet little bays, and the same instinct that had started him on his journey turned him northeastward to follow the river to the sea. He came across occasional flocks of ducks and sometimes swam with them for a day or two, and, finally, off Anticosti Island in the Gulf of Saint Lawrence, encountered a flock of young loons like himself, which had gathered together a few at a time for company, and joined them; his usual inclination for solitude would not be so strong during the winter.

For a few days they loafed about, fishing and gabbling together in soft tones and swimming in circles on their sides with one foot in the air while they preened themselves, and then began to take off in small groups to fly farther south.

The young loon left with one of these groups, which flew high above the channel across Nova Scotia at George Bay, into the Atlantic, and then south down the coast.

On their first migration they would fly farther south than the old loons. Once they joined a dark line of surf scoters flying low over the waves, but usually they flew high and widely scattered, calling across the distances that separated them. Sometimes they fished just beyond the breakers, sometimes several miles at sea, occasionally going ashore on a lonely beach to sleep. The little flock was constantly changing; new birds joined it, and many that had started with it dropped out. After they crossed Cape Cod they found a larger flock off Nantucket and coasted down to join it, but the young loon kept on alone until he was off one of the smaller New Jersey beach resorts, where he came down to feed and rest for a few days.

The fall migration was at its height, and there were many birds in the air: scoters and sea ducks over the sea, gulls and shorebirds and an occasional hawk over the beaches, long skeins of ducks and geese over the marshes behind them. Many of the gulls would winter where they were, but the main tide of travelers continued to flow toward the warm south. For the moment the young loon was content to stay, basking in the October sun, watching the fishing boats on the horizon, and making long dives to pursue and strike the fish off the beach.

A storm came along the coast and whipped up the sea; the wind plucked stinging spray off the choppy waves. The young loon was ready to move again, but made one final dive to fill his belly for a long flight, and after he had caught a fish, turned up toward the surface again. He saw a darker area above him that looked smoother than the rest of the surrounding waves and headed for it. Unfortunately for him, it was a patch of oil; a tanker, which had unloaded its cargo and stood out to sea again, had washed out its tanks off the coast during the night. This was illegal, for the sticky oil washed ashore and polluted the beaches and killed birds and fish, but many tanker captains callously did it and weren't caught. They were far away when the oil became visible the next day, and enforcement officers couldn't prove they were guilty.

The young loon came up in the middle of the floating oil, and his feathers were soon soaked with it. He was no longer buoyant and began to sink; his feathers no longer insulated him, and he grew very cold. He couldn't understand what had suddenly happened to him, for the friendly water where he had spent most of his life had betrayed him. He only knew that he must get ashore, and heavy as a stone, cold, gummy with black oil, and filled with fear, he desperately fought his way in, tossed and beaten about by the surf, and finally, chilled and exhausted, stumbled onto the beach.

He had come a quarter of a mile north of the last cottage, on an undeveloped part of the shore backed with beach grass and bayberry bushes, and, realizing his helpless condition, managed to reach the back of the beach and find a shallow little hollow in the sand among the flotsam that would conceal him and give him a little protection from the wind and the blowing cold rain. Here, chilled, weary and confused, battered by the waves that had in the past supported him, he dropped down on his keel and let the rain beat upon him.

The boy's father owned the last cottage, and the family had come to spend the weekend there for the last visit of the year. The storm had held them in the house all day, but the next morning dawned clear, and after breakfast the boy decided to take a walk up the beach. He liked to watch the long lines of scoters flying south beyond the surf and look for driftwood or any other interesting thing that had been washed up by the storm. The oil had come in during the night and covered a long area of the beach with its sticky black blanket, and to get around it the boy turned up toward the top of the beach.

He walked straight for the loon, but didn't see it crouched flat in its hollow with wind-blown sand sticking to its oily feathers. When he was within seven or eight feet away, the loon suddenly rose up and ran at him, hissing, to defend itself with its sharp bill and drive him away. Frightened by the attack, by the big bird's size and abrupt appearance out of nowhere, he jumped straight up in the air. The loon ran beneath him, kept on for a few feet, and then fell down. The boy ran off a few steps, and then, with his heart pounding, paused to look at it. At first he didn't know what the oil-soaked creature was, but after a moment he recalled the head and dangerous bill as shown by his bird book and recognized the loon for what it was: one of the great northern divers whose eerie laughing call he had heard on the lonely Canadian lake and dreamed about several times since.

He saw now what had happened to it and knew, despite its courageous defense, that it was helpless and would die away from the sea. Exposure and starvation would kill it. It lay on the sand, still and watchful, but ready to defend itself again in the only way it could. It had frightened him, but now the fright was replaced by pity, and he wanted to help it. He knew he couldn't do it by himself; he made a wide detour around it and ran back to the cottage, and found his father in the living room.

"Dad," he said, nearly out of breath from his run, "there's a loon up the beach covered with oil. It can't swim or fly or anything, and we'll have to help it."

"Sit down a minute and catch your breath. How did you find it?"

"It was in a hollow and I didn't see it. It was hiding there, and it ran at me. I jumped over its head. It was hissing, it would have bitten me. I was scared."

"You were lucky to get out of its way. During the war Coast Guardsmen had to patrol the beaches at night to look for submarines, and several of them stumbled across oil-soaked loons and they got hurt. The loons drove their bills right through heavy leather boots. He'd be pretty rough to handle, son."

"Dad, we've got to do it. After I heard them in Canada I feel like they're friends. Next to the airplane ride and the fishing they were the best part of the trip. Dad————"

"OK, boy, we'll try it. Go out under the house and get the crab net and one of those old potato bags that we carry fish in." He went to the stairway. "We're going up the beach to catch a loon," he called up to his wife. "Can you go to the store and get some salad oil and cornmeal? Better get plenty of both."

They found the loon back in his little hollow, and the boy's father approached it with the crab net. The loon charged at him as it had at the boy and he had to run aside, but after more maneuvering and dodging about he entangled its head in the net. The boy stood on the handle and, after a struggle, for the loon was strong and full of fight, the boy's father got hold of the loon's head so that it wouldn't stab him, and wrapped its body in the bag. The loon understood all this no more than it had understood the treachery of the sea, but, so enwrapped and held, it grew quiet, as though in resignation, and they carried it back to the cottage.

The boy's mother was there, back from the store, and, while the boy held the loon's feet and his father its head, she rubbed it with the salad oil to dissolve and soak up the crude oil and then with cornmeal to absorb the mixture and fluff up its feathers. It struggled a little, and then was still. They were all messy with oil in a short time, but presently the bird was clean, and they carried it far up the beach and let it go, tossing it away from them and running a few steps the other way.

They stood at a distance and watched as it ran clumsily a few yards up the beach and dropped down to rest and recover from its adventure, then turned away. It would be all right now, and presently would once again go to sea.

Add Hot Water;
Serves Fourteen Million

Thomas Meehan

Until about one-fifteen of a recent weekday morning, when I found a cure for my long torment, I was abysmally hooked, an addict. Erratic, perpetually exhausted, filled with self-loathing, and vilely short-tempered, I was in danger of losing my job, my friends, even my marriage. "Either you say goodbye to the habit or you can say goodbye to *me!*" my wife cried one night. I started to plead with her, but at that moment my bloodshot eyes strayed to our bedroom clock and I saw that it was That Time again. I shrugged and scuttled into the living room and turned on. I was, to admit the ugly truth, a late-night television-movie addict.

In my case, at least, the addiction was localized—I went only for Hollywood movies of the late nineteen-thirties. It is to this circumstance that I attribute the suddenness with which I was able to kick the habit. Others, hooked on everything from *Hell's Angels* to *Platinum High School*, may, I'm afraid, have a more difficult time with their cold turkey, but if my case is any indication, there's hope for them too.

Like a drug addict who will sniff only cocaine, I was interested in the pure pre-1940 stuff, but careful conning of newspaper TV listings and some deft channel-switching enabled me to get all of the junk I needed to feed my habit. Four or five evenings each week, I would awaken at dawn from a confused dream involving Richard Arlen, Kay Francis, and Bonita Granville, to find myself sprawled, still fully clothed, in my living-room chair, with a heap of cigarette butts and apple cores before me and only the taunting eye of the empty screen to witness my shame and degradation.

I had no warning that an escape from my torture was at hand. On the night in question, I had already taken in a Deanna Durbin musical and had just settled down miserably to a 1938 Warner Brothers gangster movie called *Angels with Dirty Faces.* Then it happened. Midway through the first reel, one of the supporting players snarled, "Them rotten coppers will never get Rocky Sullivan—he's too smart for them," and at that instant I knew, as if by magic, everything that was going to take place during the rest of the movie, right down to that final scene when Rocky Sullivan would be dragged screaming to the electric chair. I rose at once, strode to the television set and snapped it off, and went straight to bed.

Not until I awoke in the morning, refreshed by the longest sleep I'd had in months, did I fully understand the liberating significance of that scrap of dialogue. Thinking about *Angels with Dirty Faces,* and about the vast, tawdry repertory of thirties films that I knew so well, it suddenly dawned on me that the early scenes of virtually every Hollywood movie of that era contained a similar moment of précis—a brief exchange of dialogue, or in some instances merely one line, that gave away the entire film and made further viewing unnecessary. This scrap of dramaturgy, I realized, was the distilled essence, the Nescafé, of the film, and once the experienced viewer extracted this essence he could switch off his set and go to bed, where simply by adding a generous amount of mental hot water he could turn it into a full-length feature, creating what I've lately come to think of as the Instant Movie, a potion that can be consumed in two or three fast gulps just before sleep.

Now that I've kicked the habit, I feel that the very least I can do is to help pry the monkey off the backs of my erstwhile fellow-addicts, and I have therefore cooked up the makings of a handful of Instant Movies. As an example, consider a 1938 horse-racing picture. In this imaginary film, the quintessential line of dialogue comes early in the second reel, in a scene that takes place outside a rustic stable. A freckle-faced eleven-year-old tomboy named Cindy (Marcia Mae Jones) is looking pleadingly up into the moist blue eyes of an old white-haired Southern gent (Walter Brennan).

CINDY: They won't have to shoot Firefly, will they, Gramps?

Now, adding hot water to this line, we immediately have a ninety-seven-minute feature entitled *Kentucky Sunshine*. And who among us, viewing *Kentucky Sunshine,* would be able to blink back the tears when Gramps experiences a painless but garrulous death halfway through the sixth reel, or, indeed, would be able to repress a grin at the endearing high jinks of Jazzbo (Stepin Fetchit), the good-natured but bumbling Negro stable hand? What's more, would we not all feel a sudden warm glow (something akin to heartburn) when, in the closing moments of the film, Peggy (Ann Rutherford), Cindy's wind-blown older sister, at last gets together with Jim Crankshaw (Dick Foran), the idealistic young veterinarian

from down the road, as Cindy and Jazzbo chuckle on the
back porch and, in the final fadeout, Firefly sticks his head
out of his stall and whinnies playfully? Which reminds me.
No, Cindy, they won't have to shoot Firefly. In fact, in the
last reel, in the running-of-the-Derby sequence, guess which
95–1 shot is going to win the race by a nose?

I suppose the addicts in the audience have got the idea by
now, but as a further guide toward their salvation I have
cooked up ten other prototypical Instant Movies, all from
the powerful 1938 crop, of which I shall pass along only the
Nescafé; for these flickers, the reader will have to supply his
own hot water.

1. THE INSTANT
1938 HIGH-CLASS MUSICAL BIOGRAPHY MOVIE.

SCENE: *A candle-lit garret in a squalid corner of Vienna in 1843.
On a narrow cot, a pale, lovely, dying young woman* (Anita
Louise) *is whispering huskily to a sensitive-looking young man*
(Richard Greene), *whose hair is even longer than hers.*

DYING YOUNG WOMAN *(in a heavy Vienna accent):* You must
forget me, Franz. The vorld is vaiting for your beaudiful
melodies.

2. THE INSTANT
1938 SPOILED DEBUTANTE MOVIE.

SCENE: *An outsize white-on-white bedroom in a North Shore Long
Island mansion. Midge* (Jane Bryan), *a wide-eyed, saccharine
young thing, is talking with Cynthia Marlowe* (Bette Davis), *a*

chain-smoking, hyperthyroid, but madly attractive heiress of twenty-four.

MIDGE: But gee whiz, Cynthia, Polly is your own identical twin sister!

CYNTHIA: Polly is a sentimental little fool. Gordon Hughes is the most fascinating man I've ever met, and I'm going to have him.

MIDGE: But Gordon is taking Polly to the Harbor Club dance tonight.

CYNTHIA: That's what he thinks. Aunt Agatha's had another one of her attacks, and Polly left unexpectedly this morning for California to be at her bedside. Isn't that *sweet* of Polly? Gordon will never know the difference.

MIDGE: But, Cynthia, you wouldn't . . .

3. THE INSTANT
1938 NAVAL ACADEMY MOVIE.

SCENE: *A dormitory room at Annapolis on the Friday evening before the crucial annual weekend maneuvers. A veteran chief petty officer* (Wallace Beery) *is addressing a handsome but insolent young midshipman* (Robert Taylor), *who is lounging on his cot with an infuriating half smile on his lips.*

CHIEF PETTY OFFICER *(angrily):* Look, playboy, this isn't a country club, it's the *U*-nited States Navy. Your dad stood for something at this Academy, and I'm not going to let you ruin his good name.

MIDSHIPMAN: If you're quite through with the hearts and flowers, Clancy, I still have that date with Brenda at the Kit Kat Club in half an hour, and Flotilla C won't lose the

Academy flag unless you decide to turn me in. So actually it's up to you, isn't it?

4. THE INSTANT
1938 NEWSPAPERMAN MOVIE.

SCENE: *The cluttered City Room of the New York* Daily Chronicle. *The managing editor* (William Frawley) *is having a heated argument with his star reporter* (Edmund Lowe).

MANAGING EDITOR: Listen, O'Brien, you've spent enough of the paper's time on that wild-goose chase. Drop that story or consider yourself fired!

STAR REPORTER: O.K., Chief, I admit all—all the evidence says no. But somehow I think that poor guy in the death house, Stragella, is telling the truth. Give me just three hours more. I've got a hunch.

5. THE INSTANT
1938 COLLEGE FOOTBALL MOVIE.

SCENE: *The campus of Cantwell College, somewhere in the Middle West. A coed* (Patsy Kelly) *is talking excitedly with the captain of the football team* (Jack Oakie).

COED: Gee whiz, Windy, if Blinky Walinkowitz can't play on Saturday we haven't got a chance against State. And he'll never pass Professor Gottsegen's botany exam.

FOOTBALL CAPTAIN: I wouldn't be so sure of that, Glenda. Remember how Blinky was able to remember, for exactly twenty-four hours, every single word of the songs you sang when we were all riding the merry-go-round at the student carnival last week?

COED: Yes, but what's that got to do with—

FOOTBALL CAPTAIN: Plenty. The exam is tomorrow morning, and you're a straight-A student in botany. Right? Now, here's my plan. You bring Blinky here after lights-out, and I'll get my sax, and we'll . . .

6. THE INSTANT
1938 AFRICAN SAFARI MOVIE.

SCENE: *A clearing in a notably phony-looking bit of back-lot jungle. Captain Jack Clifton* (Bruce Cabot), *a world-famous African explorer, and Bob Thayer* (John Payne), *an earnest young anthropologist, are questioning a frightened native messenger* (Sam Jaffe).

NATIVE MESSENGER: Uga wamba bonga tonga. Wamba munga tbaga kwumba sbimba mboga.

BOB: What is he saying?

CAPTAIN JACK: He says that it is still two days' march to the Valley of the Lost Elephants, through Umphalombi Swamp and over Jackal's Tooth Range. Sleeping sickness has decimated the bearers we hoped to meet at the watering hole. And he says between here and the Valley there is a fierce tribe of headhunters that is holding prisoner a bearded old man and a beautiful young blond woman.

BOB: Gosh, then . . .

CAPTAIN JACK: Yes, Bob, I'm afraid it's just as we feared. The Ugwambas have captured Janet and Professor Bartelstone.

7. THE INSTANT
1938 MYSTERIOUS FATAL DISEASE MOVIE.

SCENE: *The office of James Hartwell, M.D. Dr. Hartwell* (Henry O'Neill), *a silver-haired gentleman, is talking privately with Sally*

Forsythe (Loretta Young), *a beautiful young wife and mother, who has lately been having the most painful headaches.*

DR. HARTWELL *(gravely):* I'd say six months, Sally . . . if you're careful.

SALLY: I see. Dr. Jim, promise you won't say a word about this to Jeff. He's been working so hard these last six years on his arthritis experiments. This trip to Sweden for the Nobel Prize was to have been our second honeymoon.

8. THE INSTANT
1938 LOWER EAST SIDE MOVIE.

SCENE: *The roof of a tenement on an oppressively hot and humid New York summer's night. A moody young slum dweller* (John Garfield) *is looking out on the lights of the city, as his best girl* (Priscilla Lane) *stands adoringly at his side.*

YOUNG SLUM DWELLER: You wait and see, Lois, I'm going to do just like Ma wanted me to. I'm going to write a symphony of the city. And there's gonna be everything in it —the lights, the rattle of the subways at night, the taxicabs honking, Mrs. Callaghan yelling at her kids.

BEST GIRL: Gee, that's swell, Danny. Then you're . . . you're going to give up boxing for good?

9. THE INSTANT
1938 SOPHISTICATED ROMANCE MOVIE.

SCENE: *The private New York office of Chris Baxter, the president of Amalgamated, Inc. Tim Roderick* (Melvyn Douglas), *a handsome corporation lawyer in his mid-thirties, has just burst unannounced into the room and is speaking angrily to a trim, beautiful young woman* (Rosalind Russell), *who is seated behind an enormous mahogany desk.*

TIM: All right, Miss whatever your name is, I want to see your boss, Chris Baxter, right away. Right away, you hear?

YOUNG WOMAN: If you'll please calm down, perhaps you can tell me what it is you want. I'm Chris Baxter.

TIM: You're Chris Baxter? But you're . . . you're a woman.

YOUNG WOMAN *(coolly lighting a cigarette):* And is there anything so unusual about that?

10. THE INSTANT
1938 BIG HOUSE MOVIE.

SCENE: *A cellblock at State Penitentiary. A soft-spoken Irish-American priest* (Pat O'Brien) *is reasoning quietly with an escaping convict* (James Cagney), *who is wildly waving a loaded revolver.*

PRIEST: Hand over that gun, my son.

CONVICT: Stand back, Father Jerry, or I'll drill you! I swear I'll drill you!
(Click!)

No, that wasn't the revolver misfiring—it was me turning off my television set. Good night.

Novotny's Pain

Philip Roth

In the early months of the Korean War, a young man who had been studying to be a television cameraman in a night school just west of the Loop in Chicago was drafted into the Army and almost immediately fell ill. He awoke one morning with a pain on the right side of his body, directly above the buttock. When he rolled over, it was as though whatever bones came together inside him there were not meeting as they should. The pain, however, was not what had awakened him; his eyes always opened themselves five minutes before the appearance in the barracks of the Charge of Quarters. Though there was much of Army life that he had to grit his teeth to endure, he did not have to work at getting up on time; it simply happened to him. When it was necessary to grit his teeth, he gritted them and did what he was told. In that way, he was like a good many young men who suffered military life alongside him or had suffered it before him. His sense of shame was strong, as was his sense of necessity; the two made him dutiful.

Also, he was of foreign extraction, and though his hard-working family had not as yet grown fat off the fat of the land, it was nevertheless in their grain to feel indebted to this country. Perhaps if they had been a little fatter they would have felt less indebted. As it was, Novotny believed in fighting for freedom, but because what he himself wanted most from any government was that it should let him alone to live his life. His patriotism then—his commitment to wearing this republic's uniform and carrying this republic's gun—was seriously qualified by his feeling of confinement and his feeling of loss, both of which were profound.

When the C.Q. got around to Novotny's bed that morning, he did not shine his flashlight into the soldier's eyes; he simply put a hand to his arm and said, "You better get yourself up, young trooper." Novotny was appreciative of this gentleness, and though, as he stepped from his bunk, the pain across his back was momentarily quite sharp, he met the day with his usual decision. Some mornings, making the decision required that he swallow hard and close his eyes, but he never failed to make it: *I am willing.* He did not know if any of those around him had equivalent decisions to make, because he did not ask. He did not mull much over motive. People were honest or dishonest, good or bad, himself included.

After dressing, he moved off with four others to the mess hall, where it was their turn to work for the day. It was still dark, and in the barracks the other recruits slept on. The previous day, the entire company had marched fifteen miserable miles with full packs, and then, when it was dark, they had dropped down on their stomachs and fired at pinpoints of light that flickered five hundred yards away and were supposed to be the gunfire of the enemy. Before they had climbed into trucks at midnight, they were ordered to attention and told in a high, whiny voice by their captain, a National Guardsman recently and unhappily called back to duty, that only one out of every fifty rounds they had fired had hit the targets. This news had had a strong effect upon the weary recruits, and the trucks had been silent all the way to the barracks, where it had been necessary for them to clean their rifles and scrape the mud from their boots before they flung themselves onto the springs of their bunks for a few hours' rest.

At the mess hall, the K.P.s were each served two large spoonfuls of Army eggs and a portion of potatoes. The potatoes had not been cooked long enough, and the taste they left on the palate was especially disheartening at such an early hour, with no light outdoors and a cold wind blowing. But Novotny did not complain. For one thing, he was occupied with finding a comfortable position in which to sit and eat—he had the pain only when he twisted the wrong way. Besides, the food was on his tray to give him strength, not pleasure. Novotny did not skip meals, no matter how ill-prepared they were, for he did not want to lose weight and be unequal to the tasks assigned him.

Before entering the Army, Novotny had worked for several years as an apprentice printer with a company that manufactured telephone books in Chicago. It had turned out to be dull work, and because he considered himself a bright and ambitious young man, he had looked around for a night school where he might learn a job with a future. He had settled on television, and for over a year he had been attending classes two evenings a week. He had a girl friend and a mother, to both of whom he had a strong attachment; his girl friend he loved, his mother he took care of. Novotny did not want to cause any trouble. On the other hand, he did not want to be killed. With his girl friend, he had been a man of passion; he dreamed of her often. He was thrifty, and had four hundred dollars in a savings account in the First Continental Bank on Lasalle Street in Chicago. He knew for a fact that he had been more adept at his work than anyone else in his television course. He hated the Army because nothing he did there was for himself.

The labors of the K.P.s began at dawn, and at midnight—light having come and gone—they were still at it. The cooks had ordered the men around all day until five in the afternoon, when the Negro mess sergeant showed up. He hung his Eisenhower jacket on a hook, rolled up the sleeves of his shirt, and said, "As there is a regimental inspection tomorrow morning, we will now get ourselves down to the fine points of housecleaning, gentlemens." The K.P.s had then proceeded to scrub the mess hall from floor to ceiling, inside and out.

A little after midnight, while Novotny was working away at the inside of a potato bin with a stiff brush and a bucket of hot, soapy water, the man working beside him began to cry. He said the sergeant was never going to let them go to sleep. The sergeant would be court-martialled for keeping them up like this. They would all get weak and sick. All Novotny knew of the fellow beside him was that his name was Reynolds and that he had been to college. Apparently, the mess sergeant only knew half that much, but that was enough; he came into the storeroom and saw Reynolds weeping into the empty potato bins. "College boy," he said, "wait'll they get you over in Korea." The sergeant delivered his words standing over them, looking down, and for the moment Novotny stopped feeling sorry for himself.

When the scrubbing was finished, Novotny and Reynolds had to carry back the potatoes, which were in garbage cans, and dump them into the bins. Reynolds began to explain to Novotny that he had a girl friend whom he was supposed to have called at ten-thirty. For some reason, Reynolds said, his

not having been able to get to a phone had made him lose
control. Novotny had, till then, been feeling superior to
Reynolds. For all his resenting of the stupidity that had
made them scrub out bins one minute so as to dump dirty
potatoes back into them the next, he had been feeling somewhat in league with the sergeant. Now Reynolds' words
broke through to his own unhappiness, and he was about to
say a kind word to his companion when the fellow suddenly
started crying again. Reynolds threw his hand up to cover
his wet cheeks and dropped his end of the can. Novotny's
body stiffened; with a great effort he yanked up on the can
so that it wouldn't come down on Reynolds' toes. Pain cut
deep across the base of Novotny's spine.

Later, he limped back to the barracks. He got into bed and
counted up the number of hours he had spent scrubbing out
what hadn't even needed to be scrubbed. At a dollar and a
quarter an hour, he would have made over twenty dollars.
Nineteen hours was as much night-school time as he had
been able to squeeze into three weeks. He had known Rose
Anne, his girl, for almost a year, but never had he spent
nineteen consecutive hours in her company. Though once
they had had twelve hours. . . . He had driven in his Hudson
down to Champaign, where she was a freshman at the University of Illinois, and they had stayed together, in the motel
room he had rented, from noon to midnight, not even going
out for meals. He had driven her back to her dormitory, his
shoelaces untied and wearing no socks. Never in his life had
he been so excited.

The following week, he had been drafted.

After completing his eight weeks of basic training,
Novotny was given a week's leave. His first evening home,
his mother prepared a large meal and then sat down opposite him at the table and watched him eat it. After dinner, he
stood under the hot shower for twenty minutes, letting the
water roll over him. In his bedroom, he carefully removed

the pins from a new white-on-white shirt and laid it out on the bedspread, along with a pair of Argyles, a silver tie clasp, cufflinks, and his blue suit. He polished his shoes—not for the captain's pleasure, but for his own—and chose a tie. Then he dressed for his date as he had learned to dress for a date from an article he had read in a Sunday picture magazine, while in high school, that he kept taped to the inside of his closet door. He had always collected articles having to do with how to act at parties, or dances, or on the job; his mother had never had any reason not to be proud of Novotny's behavior. She kissed him when he left the house, told him how handsome he looked, and then tears moved over her eyes as she thanked him for the government checks—for always having been a good son.

Novotny went to a movie with Rose Anne, and afterward he drove to the forest preserve where they remained until 2 A.M. In bed, later, he cursed the Army. He awoke the following morning to find that the pain, which had not troubled him for some weeks, had returned. It came and went through the next day and the following night, when once again he saw Rose Anne. Two days later, he visited the family doctor, who said Novotny had strained a muscle, and gave him a diathermy treatment. On their last night together, Rose Anne said that if writing would help, she would write not just twice a day, as was her habit, but three times a day, even four. In the dark of the forest preserve, she told Novotny that she dreamed about his body; in the dark, he told her that he dreamed of hers.

He left her weeping into a Kleenex in her dim front hallway, and drove home in a mood darker than any he had ever known. He would be killed in Korea and never see Rose Anne again, or his mother. And how unfair—for he *had* been a good son. Following his father's death, he had worked every day after school, plus Wednesday nights and Saturdays. When he had been drafted, he had vowed he would do whatever they told him to do, no matter how much he might resent it. He had kept his mouth shut and become proficient at soldiering. The better he was at soldiering, the better chance he had of coming out alive and in one piece. But that night when he left Rose Anne, he felt he had no chance at all. He would leave some part of his body on the battlefield, or come home to Rose Anne in a box. Good as he had been—industrious, devoted, stern, sacrificing—he would never have the pleasure of being a husband, or a television cameraman, or a comfort to his mother in her old age.

Five days after his return to the post—where he was to receive eight weeks of advanced infantry training, preparatory to being shipped out—he went on sick call. He sat on a long bench in the barren waiting room, and while two sullen prisoners from the stockade mopped the floor around his feet, he had his temperature taken. There were thirteen men on sick call, and they all watched the floor being washed and held thermometers under their tongues. When Novotny got to see the medic, who sat outside the doctor's office, he told him that every time he twisted or turned or stepped down on his right foot, he felt a sharp pain just above the buttock on the right side of his body. Novotny was sent back to duty with three inches of tape across his back, and a packet of APC pills.

At mail call the following morning, Novotny received a letter from Rose Anne unlike any he had ever received from her before. It was not only that her hand was larger and less controlled than usual; it was what she said. She had written down, for his very eyes to see, all those things she dreamed about when she dreamed about his body. He saw, suddenly, scenes of passion that he and she were yet to enact, moments that would not merely repeat the past but would be even deeper, even more thrilling. Oh Rose Anne—how had he found her?

Novotny's company spent the afternoon charging around with fixed bayonets—crawling, jumping up, racing ahead, through fences, over housetops, down into trenches —screaming murderously all the while. At one point, leaping from a high wall Novotny almost took his eye out with his own bayonet; he had been dreaming of his beautiful future.

The next morning, he walked stiffly to sick call and asked to see the doctor. When, in response to a question, he said it was his back that hurt him, the medic who was interviewing him replied sourly, "Everybody's back hurts." The medic told Novotny to take off his shirt so that he could lay on a few more inches of tape. Novotny asked if he could please see the doctor for just a minute. He was informed that the doctor was only seeing men with temperatures of a hundred or more. Novotny had no temperature, and he returned to his unit, as directed.

On the seventh weekend, with only one more week of training left, Novotny was given a seventy-two-hour pass. He caught a plane to Chicago and a bus to Champaign, carrying with him only a small ditty bag and Rose Anne's impassioned letter. Most of Friday, most of Saturday, and all day Sunday, Rose Anne wept, until Novotny was more miserable than he had ever imagined a man could be. On Sunday night, she held him in her arms and he proceeded to tell her at last of how he had been mistreated by the medic; till then he had not wanted to cause her more grief than she already felt. She stroked his hair while he told how he had not even been allowed to see a doctor. Rose Anne wept and said the medic should be shot. They had no right to send Novotny to Korea if they wouldn't even look after his health here at home. What would happen to him if his back started to act up in the middle of a battle? How could he take care of himself? She raised many questions—rational ones, irrational ones, but none that Novotny had not already considered himself.

Novotny travelled all night by train so as to be back at the base by reveille. He spent most of the next day firing a Browning automatic, and the following morning, when he was to go on K.P., he could not even lift himself from his bed, so cruel was the pain in his back.

In the hospital, the fellow opposite Novotny had been in a wheelchair for two years with osteomyelitis. Every few months, they shortened his legs; nevertheless, the disease continued its slow ascent. The man on Novotny's right had dropped a hand grenade in basic training and blown bits of both his feet off. Down at the end of Novotny's aisle lay a man who had had a crate full of ammunition tip off a truck onto him, and the rest of the men in the ward, many of whom were in the hospital to learn to use prosthetic devices, had been in Korea.

The day after Novotny was assigned to the ward, the man the crate had fallen on was wheeled away to be given a myelogram. He came back to the ward holding his head in his hands. As soon as Novotny was able to leave his bed, he made his way over to this fellow's bed, and because he had heard that the man's condition had been diagnosed as a back injury, he asked him how he was feeling. He got around to asking what a myelogram was, and why he had come back to the ward holding his head. The fellow was talkative enough, and told him that they had injected a white fluid directly into his spine and then X-rayed him as the fluid moved down along the vertebrae, so as to see if the spinal discs were damaged. He told Novotny that apparently it was the stuff injected into him that had given him the headache, but then he added that, lousy as he had felt, he considered himself pretty lucky. He had heard of cases, he said, where the needle had slipped. Novotny had himself heard of instances where doctors had left towels and sponges inside patients, so he could believe it. The man said that all the needle had to do was go off by a hairbreadth and it would wind up in the tangle of nerves leading into the spine. Two days later, two damaged discs were cut out of the man with the injured back, and three of his vertebrae were fused together. All through the following week he lay motionless in his bed.

One evening earlier, while Novotny was still restricted to bed, he had been visited by Reynolds. Reynolds had come around to say goodbye; the entire outfit was to be flown out the next day. Since Reynolds and Novotny hardly knew each other, they had been silent after Reynolds spoke of what was to happen to him and the others the following day. Then Reynolds had said that Novotny was lucky to have developed back trouble when he did; he wouldn't have minded a touch of it himself. Then he left.

When Novotny was out of bed and walking around, X-rays were taken of his back, and the doctors told him they showed no sign of injury or disease; there was a slight narrowing of the intervertebral space between what they referred to on the pictures as L-1 and L-2, but nothing to suggest damage to the disc—which was what Novotny had worked up courage to ask them about. The doctors took him into the examination room and bent him forward and backward. They ran a pin along his thigh and calf and asked if he felt any sensation. They laid him down on a table and, while they slowly raised his leg, asked if he felt any pain. When his leg was almost at a ninety-degree angle with his body, Novotny thought that he did feel his pain, and remembered the misery of no one's taking it seriously but himself. Then he thought of all the men around him who hobbled on artificial limbs during the day and moaned in their beds at night, and he said nothing. Consequently, they sent him back to duty.

He was shunted into an infantry company that was in its seventh week of advanced training. Two days before the company was to be shipped out, he awoke in the morning to discover that the pain had returned. He was able to limp to sick call, where he found on duty the unsympathetic medic, who, almost immediately upon seeing Novotny, began to unwind a roll of three-inch tape. Novotny raised an objection, and an argument ensued, which was settled when the doctor emerged from behind his door. He ordered Novotny into his office and had him strip. He told him to bend forward and touch his toes. Novotny tried, but could come only to within a few inches of them. The doctor looked over Novotny's medical record and then asked if he expected the Army to stand on its head because one soldier couldn't touch his toes. He asked him what he expected the Army to do for him. The doctor said there were plenty of G.I.s with sore backs in Korea. And with worse. Plenty worse.

Though the pain diminished somewhat during the day, it returned the next morning with increased severity. Novotny could by this time visualize his own insides—he saw the bone as white, and the spot where the pain was located as black. At breakfast, he changed his mind three times over, then went off to the first sergeant to ask permission to go on sick call. He had decided finally that if he did not go and have the condition taken care of within the next few days it would simply get worse and worse; surely there would be no time for medical attention, no proper facilities, while they were in transit to Korea. And, once in Korea, those in charge would surely be even more deaf to his complaints than they were here; there they would be deafened by the roar of cannons. The first sergeant asked Novotny what the matter was this time, and he answered that his back hurt. The first sergeant said what the medic had said the first day: "Everybody's back hurts." But he let him go.

At sick call, the doctor sat Novotny down and asked him what *he* thought was wrong with him. What the suffering soldier had begun to think was that perhaps he had cancer or leukemia. It was really in an effort to minimize his complaint that he said that maybe he had a slipped disc. The doctor said that if Novotny had slipped a disc he wouldn't even be able to walk around. Novotny suddenly found it difficult to breathe. What had he done in life to deserve this? What had he done, from the day he had grown out of short pants, but everything that was asked of him? He told the doctor that all he knew was that he had a pain. He tried to explain that taping it up didn't seem to work; the pain wasn't on the surface but deep inside his back. The doctor said it was deep inside his head. When the doctor told him to go back to duty like a man, Novotny refused.

Novotny was taken to the hospital, and to the office of the colonel in charge of orthopedics. He was a bald man with weighty circles under his eyes and a very erect carriage, who looked to have lived through a good deal. The colonel asked Novotny to sit down and tell him about the pain. Novotny, responding to a long-suffering quality in the man that seemed to him to demand respect, told him the truth: he had rolled over one morning during his basic training, and there it had been, deep and sharp. The colonel asked Novotny if he could think of anything at all that might have caused the pain. Novotny recounted what had happened on K.P. with Reynolds. The doctor asked if that had occurred before the morning he had awakened with the pain, or after it. Novotny admitted that it was after. But surely, he added, that must have aggravated the pain. The doctor said that that did not clear up the problem of where the pain had come from in the first place. He reminded Novotny that the X-rays showed nothing. He ordered Novotny to take off his hospital blues and stretch out on the examination table. By this time, of course, Novotny knew all the tests by heart; once, in fact, he anticipated what he was about to be asked to do, and the colonel gave him a strange look.

When the doctor was finished, he told Novotny that he

had a lumbosacral strain with some accompanying muscle
spasm. Nothing more. It was what they used to call a touch
of lumbago. Novotny stood up to leave, and the colonel informed him that when he was released from the hospital he
would have to appear at a summary court-martial for having
refused to obey the doctor's order to return to duty.
Novotny felt weak enough to faint. He was suddenly sorry
he had ever opened his mouth. He was ashamed. He heard
himself explaining to the colonel that he had refused to obey
only because he had felt too sick to go back to duty. The
colonel said it was for a trained doctor to decide how sick or
well Novotny was. But, answered Novotny—hearing the
gates to the stockade slamming shut behind him, imagining
prison scenes so nasty even he couldn't endure them—but
the doctor had made a mistake. As the colonel said, he *did*
have a lumbosacral strain, and muscle spasm, too. In a steely
voice, the colonel told him that there were men in Korea
who had much worse. That was the statement to which
Novotny had no answer; it was the statement that everyone
finally made to him.

When they put him in traction, he had further premoni-
tions of his court-martial and his subsequent internment in
the stockade. He, Novotny, who had never broken a law in
his life. What was happening? Each morning, he awoke at
the foot of the bed, pulled there by the weights tied to his
ankles and hanging to the floor. His limbs and joints ached
day in and day out from being stretched. More than once,
he had the illusion of being tortured for a crime he had not
committed, although he knew that the traction was therapeutic. At the end of a week, the weights were removed and he
was sent to the physical-therapy clinic, where he received
heat treatments and was given a series of exercises to perform. Some days, the pain lessened almost to the point of
disappearing. Other days, it was as severe as it had ever
been. Then he believed that they would have to cut him

open, and it would be the doctor at sick call who would be court-martialled instead of himself. When the pain was at its worst, he felt vindicated; but then, too, when it was at its worst he was most miserable.

He was only alone when he was in the bathroom, and it was there that he would try to bend over and touch his toes. He repeated and repeated this, as though it were a key to something. One day, thinking himself alone, he had begun to strain toward his toes when he was turned around by the voice of the osteomyelitis victim, who was sitting in the doorway in his wheelchair. "How's your backache, buddy?" he said, and wheeled sharply away. Everybody in the ward somehow knew bits of Novotny's history; nobody, nobody knew the whole story.

Nobody he didn't know liked him; and he stopped liking those he did know. His mother appeared at the hospital two weeks after his admittance. She treated him like a hero, leaving him with a shoebox full of baked goods and a Polish sausage. He could not bring himself to tell her about his court-martial; he could not disappoint her—and that made him angry. He was even glad to see her go, lonely as he was. Then, the following weekend, Rose Anne arrived. Everybody whistled when she walked down the ward. And he was furious at her—but for what? For being so desirable? So perfect? They argued, and Rose Anne went back to Champaign, bewildered. That night, the Negro fellow next to Novotny, who had lost his right leg in the battle of Seoul, leaned over the side of his bed and said to him, with a note in his voice more dreamy than malicious, "Hey, man, you got it made."

The next day, very early, Novotny went to the hospital library and searched the shelves until he found a medical encyclopedia. He looked up "slipped disc." Just as he had suspected, many of his own symptoms were recorded there. His heart beat wildly as he read of the difficulties of diagnosing a slipped disc, even with X-rays. Ah yes, only the myelogram was certain. He read on and on, over and over, symptoms, treatments, and drugs. One symptom he read of was a tingling sensation that ran down the back of the leg and into the foot, caused by pressure of the herniated disc on a nerve. The following morning, he awoke with a tingling sensation that ran down the back of his right leg and into his foot. Only momentarily was he elated; then it hurt.

On his weekly ward rounds, the colonel, followed by the nurse and the resident, walked up to each bed and talked to the patient; everyone waited his turn silently, as in formation. The colonel examined stumps, incisions, casts, prosthetic devices, and then asked each man how he felt. When he reached Novotny, he asked him to step out of bed and into the aisle, and there he had him reach down and touch his toes. Novotny tried, bending and bending. Someone in the ward called out, "Come on, Daddy, you can do it." Another voice called, "Push, Polack, *push*"—and then it seemed to him that all the patients in the ward were shouting and laughing, and the colonel was doing nothing to restrain them. "Ah, wait'll they get you in Korea"—and then suddenly the ward was silent, for Novotny was straightening up, his face a brilliant red. "I can't do it, sir," he said. "Does your back feel better?" the colonel asked. "Yes, sir." "Do you think we should send you back to duty?" "I've had a tingling sensation down the back of my right leg," Novotny said. "So?" the colonel asked. The ward was silent; Novotny decided not to answer.

In the afternoon, Novotny was called to the colonel's office. He walked there without too much difficulty—but then it was not unusual for the pain to come and go and come back again, with varying degrees of severity. Sometimes the cycle took hours, sometimes days, sometimes only minutes. It was enough to drive a man crazy.

In the colonel's office, Novotny was told that he was going to get another chance. Novotny was too young, the colonel said, not to be extended a little forgiveness for his self-concern. If he went back to duty, the charges against him would be dismissed and there would be no court-martial. The colonel said that with a war on there was nothing to be gained by putting a good soldier behind bars. The colonel let Novotny know that he was impressed by his marksmanship record, which he had taken the trouble to look up in the company files.

When it was Novotny's turn to speak, he could only think to ask if the colonel believed the tingling sensation in his leg meant nothing at all. The colonel, making it obvious that it was patience he was displaying, asked Novotny what *he* thought it meant. Novotny said he understood it to be a symptom of a slipped disc. The colonel asked him how he knew that, and Novotny—hesitating only a moment, then going on with the truth, on and on with it—said that he had read it in a book. The colonel, his mouth turning down in disgust, asked Novotny if he was that afraid of going to Korea. Novotny did not know what to answer; he truly had not thought of it that way before. The colonel then asked him if he ever broke out in a cold sweat at night. Novotny said no—the only new symptom he had was the tingling in the leg. The colonel brought a fist down on his desk and told Novotny that the following day he was sending him over to see the psychiatrist. He could sit out the rest of the war in the nuthouse.

What to do? Novotny did not know. It was not a cold but a hot sweat that he was in all through dinner. In the evening, he walked to the Coke machine in the hospital basement, as lonely as he had ever been. A nurse passed him in the hall and smiled. She thought he was sick. He drank his Coke, but when he saw two wheelchairs headed his way he turned and moved up the stairs to the hospital library. He began to perspire again, and then he set about looking through the shelves for a book on psychology. Since he knew as little about psychology as he did about medicine, he had to look for a very long time. He did not want to ask for the help of the librarian, even though she was a civilian. At last he was able to pick out two books, and he sat down on the floor between the stacks, where nobody could see him.

Much of what he read he did not completely follow, but once in a while he came upon an anecdote, and in his frustration with the rest of the book, he would read that feverishly. He read of a woman in a European country who had imagined that she was pregnant. She had swelled up, and then, after nine months, she had had labor pains—but no baby. Because it had all been in her imagination. *Her imagination had made her swell up!* Novotny read this over several times. He did not believe that a man would take the time to sit down and write a book so as to tell other people lies.

When he walked back to the ward, his back seemed engulfed in flames. It was then that he became absorbed in the fantasy of reaching inside himself and cutting out of his body the offending circle of pain. He saw himself standing over his own naked back and twisting down on an instrument that resembled the little utensil that is sold in dime stores to remove the core of a grapefruit. In his bed, he could not find a position in which the pain could be forgotten or ignored. He got up and went to the phone booth, where he called long distance to Rose Anne. He could barely prevent himself from begging her to get on a plane and fly down to him that very night. And yet—the darkness, his fright, his fatigue were taking their toll—if it wasn't his back that was causing the pain, was it Rose Anne? Was he being punished for being so happy with her? Were they being punished for all that sex? Unlike his mother, he was not the kind of Catholic who believed in Hell; he was not the kind who was afraid of sex. All he wanted was his chance at life. That was all.

In the washroom, before he returned to bed, he tried to touch his toes. He forced himself down and down and down until his eyes were cloudy from pain and his fingers had moved to within an inch of the floor. But he could not keep his brain from working, and he did not know what to think. If a woman could imagine herself to be in labor, then for him, too, anything was possible. He leaned over the sink and looked into the mirror. With the aid of every truthful cell in his pained body, he admitted to his own face that he was—yes, he was—frightened of going to Korea. Terribly frightened. But wasn't everybody? He wondered if nothing could be wrong with him. He wondered if nothing he knew was so.

The next day, the psychiatrist asked Novotny if he felt nervous. He said he didn't. The psychiatrist asked if he had felt nervous before he had come into the Army. Novotny said no, that he had been happy. He asked if Novotny was afraid of high places, and if he minded being in crowds; he asked if he had any brothers and sisters, and which he liked better, his mother or his father. Novotny answered that his father was dead. He asked which Novotny had liked better before his father was dead. He asked which Novotny had liked better before his father died. Novotny did not really care to talk about this subject, particularly to someone he didn't even know, but he had decided to be as frank and truthful with the psychiatrist as it was still possible for him to be—at least, he meant to tell him what he *thought* was the truth. Novotny answered that his father had been lazy and incompetent, and the family was finally better off with him gone. The psychiatrist then asked Novotny about Rose Anne. Novotny was frank. He asked Novotny if his back hurt when he was being intimate with Rose Anne. Novotny answered that sometimes it did and sometimes it didn't. He asked Novotny if, when it did hurt, they ceased being intimate. Novotny dropped his head. It was with a searing sense that some secret had been uncovered, something he himself had not even known, that he admitted that they did not. He simply could not bring himself, however, to tell the psychiatrist what exactly they did do when Novotny's back was at its worst. He said quickly that he planned to marry Rose Anne—that he had always known he would marry her. The psychiatrist asked where the couple would live, and Novotny said with his mother. When he asked Novotny why, Novotny said because he had to take care of her, too.

The psychiatrist made Novotny stand up, close his eyes, and try to touch the tips of his index fingers together. While Novotny's eyes were closed, the psychiatrist leaned forward and, in a whisper, asked if Novotny was afraid of dying. The weight of all that he had been put through in the past weeks came down upon the shoulders of the young soldier. He broke down and admitted to a fear of death. He began to weep and to say that he didn't want to die. The psychiatrist asked him if he hated the Army, and he admitted that he did.

The psychiatrist's office was across the street from the main hospital, in the building the colonel had called the nuthouse. Novotny, full of shame, was led out of the building by an attendant with a large ring of keys hooked to his belt; he had to unlock three doors before Novotny got out to the street. He went out the rear door, just in sight of a volleyball game that was being played within a wire enclosure at the back of the building. To pull himself together before returning to the hostile cripples in the ward, Novotny watched the teams bat the ball back and forth over the net, and then he realized that they were patients who spent their days and nights inside the building from which he had just emerged. It occurred to him that the doctors were going to put him into the psychiatric hospital. Not because he was making believe he had a pain in his back—which, he had come to

think, was really why they had been going to put him in the
stockade—but precisely because he was *not* making believe.
He was feeling a pain for which there was no cause. He had
a terrible vision of Rose Anne having to come here to visit
him. She was only a young girl, and he knew that it would
frighten her so much to be led through three locked doors
that he would lose her. He was about to begin to lose things.

He pulled himself straight up—he had been stooping
—and clenched his teeth and told himself that in a
certain number of seconds the pain would be gone for good.
He counted to thirty, and then took a step. He came down
upon his right foot with only half his weight, but the pain
was still there, so sharp that it made his eyes water. The volleyball smashed against the fence through which he was
peering, and, trying to walk as he remembered himself walking when he was a perfectly healthy young man, a man with
nothing to fear—a man, he thought, who had not even
begun to know of all the confusion growing up inside
him—he walked away.

The colonel had Novotny called to his office the following
day. The night before, Novotny had got little sleep, but by
dawn he had reached a decision. Now, though he feared the
worst, he marched to the colonel's office with a plan of action held firmly in mind. When Novotny entered, the colonel
asked him to sit down, and proceeded to tell him of his own
experiences in the Second World War. He had flown with an
airborne division at a time when he was only a little more
than Novotny's age. He had jumped from a plane over
Normandy and broken both his legs, and then been shot in
the chest by a French farmer for a reason he still did not
understand. The colonel said that he had returned from
Korea only a week before Novotny had entered the hospital.
He wished that Novotny could see what the men there were
going through—he wished Novotny could be witness to the
bravery and the courage and the comradery, and, too, to the

misery and suffering. The misery of our soldiers and of those poor Koreans! He was not angry with Novotny personally; he was only trying to tell him something for his own good. Novotny was too young to make a decision that might disgrace him for the rest of his life. He told the young soldier that if he walked around with that back of his for a few weeks, if he just stopped *thinking* about it all the time, it would be as good as new. That, in actual fact, it was almost as good as new right now. He said that Novotny's trouble was that he was a passive-aggressive.

Novotny's voice was very thin when he asked the colonel what he meant. The colonel read to him what the psychiatrist had written. It was mostly the answers that Novotny had given to the psychiatrist's questions; some of it had to do with the way Novotny had sat, and the tone of his voice, and certain words he had apparently used. In the end, the report said that Novotny was a passive-aggressive and recommended he be given an administrative separation from the Army, and the appropriate discharge. Novotny asked what that meant. The colonel replied that the appropriate discharge as far as he was concerned was "plain and simple"; he took down a book of regulations from a shelf behind him, and after flipping past several pages read to Novotny in a loud voice. " 'An undesirable discharge is an administrative separation from the service under conditions other than honorable. It is issued for unfitness, misconduct, or security reasons.' " He looked up, got no response, and, fiery-eyed, read further. " 'It is recognized that all enlisted personnel with behavior problems cannot be rehabilitated by proper leadership and/or psychiatric assistance. It is inevitable that a certain percentage of individuals entering the service subsequently will demonstrate defective moral habits, irresponsibility, inability to profit by experience—' " He paused to read the last phrase again, and then went on— " 'untrustworthiness, lack of regard for the rights of others, and inability to put off pleasures and impulses of the moment.' " He engaged Novotny's eye. " 'Often,' " he said, returning to the regulation, " 'these individuals show poor performance despite intelligence, superficial charm, and a readiness to promise improvement. The effective leader is able to rehabilitate only the percentage of persons with behavior problems who are amenable to leadership.' " He stopped. "You can say that again," he mumbled, and pushed the book forward on his desk so that it faced Novotny. "Unfitness, soldier," he said, tapping his finger on the page. "It's what we use to get the crackpots out—bed-wetters, homos, petty thieves, malingerers, and so on." He waited for Novotny to take in the page's contents, and while he did, the colonel made it clear that such a discharge followed a man through life. Novotny, raising his head slightly, asked again what a passive-aggressive was. The colonel looked into his eyes and said, "Just another kind of coward."

What Novotny had decided in bed the night before was to request a myelogram. Of course, there lived still in his imagination the man who had said that all the needle had to do was be off by a hairbreadth; he was convinced, in fact, that something like that was just what would happen to him, given the way things had begun to go in his life. But though such a prospect frightened him, he did not see that he had any choice. The truth had to be known, one way or the other. But when the colonel finished and waited for him to speak, he remained silent.

"What do you have against the Army, Novotny?" the colonel asked. "What makes you so special?"

Novotny did not mention the myelogram. Why *should* he? Why should he have to take so much from people when he had an honest-to-God pain in his back? He was not imagining it, he was not making it up. He had practically ruptured himself when Reynolds had dropped the end of the can of potatoes. Maybe he had only awakened with a simple strain that first morning, but trying to keep the can from dropping on Reynolds' toes, he had done something serious to his back. That all the doctors were unable to give a satisfactory diagnosis did not make his pain any less real.

"You are a God-damned passive-aggressive, young man, what do you think of that?" the colonel said.

Novotny did not speak.

"You know how many people in America have low back pain?" the colonel demanded. "Something like fifteen per cent of the adult population of this country has low back pain—and what do you think they do, quit? Lay down on the job? What do you think a man does who has a family and responsibilities—stop supporting them? You know what your trouble is, my friend? You think life owes you something. You think something's coming to you. I spotted you right off, Novotny. You're going to get your way in this world. Everybody else can go to hell, just so long as you have your way. Imagine if all those men in Korea, if they all give in to every little ache and pain. Imagine if that was what our troops had done at Valley Forge, or Okinawa. Then where would we all be? Haven't you ever heard of self-sacrifice? The average man, if you threatened him with this kind of discharge, would do just about anything he could to avoid it. But not you. Even if you have pain, haven't you got the guts to go ahead and serve like everybody else? Well, answer me, yes or no?"

But Novotny would not answer. All he had done was answer people and tell them the truth, and what had it got him? What good was it, being good? What good was it, especially if at bottom you were bad anyway? What good was it, acting strong, if at bottom you were weak and couldn't *be* strong if you wanted to? With the colonel glaring across at him, the only solace Novotny had was to think that nobody knew any more about him than he himself did. Whatever anybody chose to call him didn't really mean a thing.

"Ah, get out of my sight," the colonel said. "People like

you make me sick. Go ahead, join the bed-wetters and the queers. Get the hell out of here."

Within six days, the Army had rid itself of Novotny. It took Novotny, however, a good deal more than six days to rid himself of infirmity, if he can be said ever to have rid himself of infirmity—or, at least, the threat of infirmity. During the next year, he missed days of work and evenings of night school, and spent numerous weekends on a mattress supported by a bed board, where he rested and nursed away his pain. He went to one doctor who prescribed a set of exercises, and another who prescribed a steel brace, which Novotny bought but found so uncomfortable that he finally had to stick it away in the attic, though it had cost forty-five dollars. Another doctor, who had been recommended to him, listened to his story, then simply shrugged his shoulders; and still another told Novotny what the colonel had—that many Americans had low back ailments, that they were frequently of unknown origin, and that he would have to learn to live with it.

That, finally, was what he tried to do. Gradually, over the years, the pain diminished in severity and frequency, though even today he has an occasional bad week, and gets a twinge if he bends the wrong way or picks up something he shouldn't. He is married to Rose Anne and is employed as a television cameraman by an educational channel in Chicago. His mother lives with him and his wife in Park Forest. For the most part, he leads a quiet, ordinary sort of life, though his attachment to Rose Anne is still marked by an unusual passion. When the other men in Park Forest go bowling on Friday nights, Novotny stays home, for he tries not to put strains upon his body to which he has decided it is not equal. In a way, all the awfulness of those Army days has boiled down to that—no bowling. There are nights, of course, when Novotny awakens from a dead sleep to worry in the dark about the future. What will happen to him? What won't? But surely those are questions he shares with all men, sufferers of low back pain and non-sufferers alike. Nobody has ever yet asked to see his discharge papers, so about that the colonel was wrong.

Silly but Sensible Songs

W. S. Gilbert

from Trial by Jury

SONG—Judge.

When I, good friends, was called to the bar,
   I'd an appetite fresh and hearty,
But I was, as many young barristers are,
   An impecunious party.
I'd a swallow-tail coat of a beautiful blue—
   A brief which I bought of a booby—
A couple of shirts and a collar or two,
   And a ring that looked like a ruby!

In Westminster Hall I danced a dance,
  Like a semi-despondent fury;
For I thought I should never hit on a chance
  Of addressing a British Jury—
But I soon got tired of third-class journeys,
  And dinners of bread and water;
So I fell in love with a rich attorney's
  Elderly, ugly daughter.

The rich attorney, he jumped with joy,
  And replied to my fond professions:
"You shall reap the reward of your pluck, my boy
  At the Bailey and Middlesex Sessions.
You'll soon get used to her looks," said he,
  "And a very nice girl you'll find her!
She may very well pass for forty-three
  In the dusk, with a light behind her!"

The rich attorney was good as his word;
  The briefs came trooping gaily,
And every day my voice was heard
  At the Sessions or Ancient Bailey.
All thieves who could my fees afford
  Relied on my orations,
And many a burglar I've restored
  To his friends and his relations.

At length I became as rich as the Gurneys—
  An incubus then I thought her,
So I threw over that rich attorney's
  Elderly, ugly daughter.
The rich attorney my character high
  Tried vainly to disparage—
And now, if you please, I'm ready to try
  This Breach of Promise of Marriage!

For now I am a Judge!

ALL.
And a good Judge too.

JUDGE.
Yes, now I am a Judge!

ALL.
And a good Judge too!

JUDGE.
Though all my law is fudge,
Yet I'll never, never budge,
But I'll live and die a Judge!

ALL.
And a good Judge too!

JUDGE (*pianissimo*).
It was managed by a job—

ALL.
And a good job too!

JUDGE.
It was managed by a job!

ALL.
And a good job too!

JUDGE.
It is patent to the mob,
That my being made a nob
Was effected by a job.

ALL.
And a good job too!

from H.M.S. Pinafore

SONG—Sir Joseph.

When I was a lad I served a term
As office boy to an Attorney's firm.
I cleaned the windows and I swept the floor,
And I polished up the handle of the big front door.
    I polished up that handle so carefullee
    That now I am the Ruler of the Queen's Navee!

As office boy I made such a mark
That they gave me the post of a junior clerk.
I served the writs with a smile so bland,
And I copied all the letters in a big round hand—
    I copied all the letters in a hand so free,
    That now I am the Ruler of the Queen's Navee!

In serving writs I made such a name
That an articled clerk I soon became;
I wore clean collars and a brand-new suit
For the pass examination at the Institute.
    And that pass examination did so well for me,
    That now I am the Ruler of the Queen's Navee!

Of legal knowledge I acquired such a grip
That they took me into the partnership.
And that junior partnership, I ween,
Was the only ship that I ever had seen.
    But that kind of ship so suited me,
    That now I am the Ruler of the Queen's Navee!

I grew so rich that I was sent
By a pocket borough into Parliament.
I always voted at my party's call,
And I never thought of thinking for myself at all.
    I thought so little, they rewarded me
    By making me the Ruler of the Queen's Navee!

Now landsmen all, whoever you may be,
If you want to rise to the top of the tree,
If your soul isn't fettered to an office stool,
Be careful to be guided by this golden rule—
    Stick close to your desks and never go to sea,
    And you all may be Rulers of the Queen's Navee!

from Princess Ida

SONG—Gama.

If you give me your attention, I will tell you what I am:
I'm a genuine philanthropist—all other kinds are sham.
Each little fault of temper and each social defect
In my erring fellow-creatures I endeavour to correct.
To all their little weaknesses I open people's eyes;
And little plans to snub the self-sufficient I devise;
I love my fellow-creatures—I do all the good I can—
Yet everybody says I'm such a disagreeable man!
    And I can't think why!

To compliments inflated I've a withering reply;
And vanity I always do my best to mortify;
A charitable action I can skilfully dissect;
And interested motives I'm delighted to detect;
I know everybody's income and what everybody earns;
And I carefully compare it with the income-tax returns;
But to benefit humanity however much I plan,
Yet everybody says I'm such a disagreeable man!
         And I can't think why!

I'm sure I'm no ascetic; I'm as pleasant as can be;
You'll always find me ready with a crushing repartee,
I've an irritating chuckle, I've a celebrated sneer,
I've an entertaining snigger, I've a fascinating leer.
To everybody's prejudice I know a thing or two;
I can tell a woman's age in half a minute—and I do.
But although I try to make myself as pleasant as I can,
Yet everybody says I am a disagreeable man!
         And I can't think why!

from The Mikado

DUET—Katisha and Ko-Ko.

Kat. There is beauty in the bellow of the blast,
   There is grandeur in the growling of the gale.
       There is eloquent outpouring
       When the lion is a-roaring,
   And the tiger is a-lashing of his tail!
Ko.   Yes, I like to see a tiger

From the Congo or the Niger,
And especially when lashing of his tail!
KAT. Volcanoes have a splendour that is grim,
And earthquakes only terrify the dolts,
But to him who's scientific
There's nothing that's terrific
In the falling of a flight of thunderbolts!
KO. Yes, in spite of all my meekness,
If I have a little weakness,
It's a passion for a flight of thunderbolts!
BOTH. If that is so,
Sing derry down derry!
It's evident, very,
Our tastes are one.
Away we'll go,
And merrily marry,
Nor tardily tarry
Till day is done!
Ko. There is beauty in extreme old age—
Do you fancy you are elderly enough?
Information I'm requesting
On a subject interesting:
Is a maiden all the better when she's tough?
KAT. Throughout this wide dominion
It's the general opinion
That she'll last a good deal longer when she's
tough.
Ko. Are you old enough to marry, do you think?
Won't you wait till you are eighty in the shade?
There's a fascination frantic
In a ruin that's romantic;
Do you think you are sufficiently decayed?
KAT. To the matter that you mention
I have given some attention,
And I think I am sufficiently decayed.

BOTH.   If that is so,
                Sing derry down derry!
             It's evident, very,
                    Our tastes are one!
          Away we'll go,
             And merrily marry,
             Nor tardily tarry
                    Till day is done!

from The Gondoliers

SONG—DON ALHAMBRA,
WITH MARCO AND GIUSEPPE.

DON AL.   There lived a King, as I've been told,
               In the wonder-working days of old,
               When hearts were twice as good as gold,
                    And twenty times as mellow.
               Good-temper triumphed in his face,
               And in his heart he found a place
               For all the erring human race
                    And every wretched fellow.
               When he had Rhenish wine to drink
               It made him very sad to think
               That some, at junket or at jink,
                    Must be content with toddy.

DON AL.   He wished all men as rich as he
               (And he was rich as rich could be),
               So to the top of every tree
                    Promoted everybody.

MAR. *and* GIU. Now, that's the kind of King for me—
He wished all men as rich as he,
So to the top of every tree
    Promoted everybody!

DON AL. Lord Chancellors were cheap as sprats,
And Bishops in their shovel hats
Were plentiful as tabby cats—
    In point of fact, too many.
Ambassadors cropped up like hay,
Prime Ministers and such as they
Grew like asparagus in May,
    And Dukes were three a penny.
On every side Field-Marshals gleamed,
Small beer were Lords-Lieutenant deemed,
With Admirals the ocean teemed
    All round his wide dominions.

DON AL. And Party Leaders you might meet
In twos and threes in every street
Maintaining, with no little heat,
    Their various opinions.

MAR. *and* GIU. Now that's a sight you couldn't beat—
Two Party Leaders in each street
Maintaining, with no little heat,
    Their various opinions.

DON AL. That King, although no one denies
His heart was of abnormal size,
Yet he'd have acted otherwise
    If he had been acuter.
The end is easily foretold,
When every blessed thing you hold
Is made of silver, or of gold,
    You long for simple pewter.

When you have nothing else to wear
But cloth of gold and satins rare,
For cloth of gold you cease to care—
    Up goes the price of shoddy.

DON AL.   In short, whoever you may be,
               To his conclusion you'll agree,
               When every one is somebodee,
                   Then no one's anybody!

MAR. *and* GIU. Now that's as plain as plain can be,
                To this conclusion we agree—

ALL.   When every one is somebodee,
                   Then no one's anybody!

SONG—DUCHESS.

On the day when I was wedded
    To your admirable sire,
I acknowledge that I dreaded
    An explosion of his ire.
I was overcome with panic—
For his temper was volcanic,
    And I didn't dare revolt,
    For I feared a thunderbolt!
I was always very wary,
    For his fury was ecstatic—
His refined vocabulary
    Most unpleasantly emphatic.
        To the thunder
          Of this Tartar
        I knocked under
          Like a martyr;
        When intently

He was fuming,
I was gently
    Unassuming—
When reviling
    Me completely,
I was smiling
    Very sweetly:
Giving him the very best, and getting back the very worst—
That is how I tried to tame your great progenitor—at first!

But I found that a reliance
    On my threatening appearance,
And a resolute defiance
    Of marital interference,
And a gentle intimation
Of my firm determination
    To see what I could do
    To be wife and husband too
Was the only thing required
    For to make his temper supple.
And you couldn't have desired
    A more reciprocating couple.
    Ever willing
        To be wooing,
    We were billing—
        We were cooing;
    When I merely
        From him parted,
    We were nearly
        Broken-hearted—
    When in sequel
        Reunited,
    We were equal-
        Ly delighted.
So with double-shotted guns and colours nailed unto the
    mast,
I tamed your insignificant progenitor—at last!

Hate

Arthur C. Clarke

Only Joey was awake on deck, in the cool stillness before dawn, when the meteor came flaming out of the sky above New Guinea. He watched it climb up the heavens until it passed directly overhead, routing the stars and throwing swift-moving shadows across the crowded deck. The harsh light outlined the bare rigging, the coiled ropes and air hoses, the copper diving helmets neatly snugged down for the night—even the low, pandanus-clad island half a mile away. As it passed into the southwest, out over the emptiness of the Pacific, it began to disintegrate. Incandescent globules broke off, burning and guttering in a trail of fire that stretched a quarter of the way across the sky. It was already dying when it raced out of sight, but Joey did not see its end. Still blazing furiously, it sank below the horizon as if seeking to hurl itself into the face of the hidden sun.

If the sight was spectacular, the utter silence was unnerving. Joey waited and waited and waited, but no sound came from the riven heavens. When, minutes later, there was a sudden splash from the sea close at hand, he gave an involuntary start of surprise—then cursed himself for being frightened by a manta. (A mighty big one, though, to have made so much noise when it jumped.) There was no other sound, and presently he went back to sleep.

In his narrow bunk just aft of the air compressor, Tibor heard nothing. He slept so soundly after his day's work that he had little energy even for dreams—and when they came, they were not the dreams he wanted. In the hours of darkness, as his mind roamed back and forth across the past, it never came to rest amid memories of desire. He had women in Sydney and Brisbane and Darwin and Thursday Island —but none in his dreams. All that he ever remembered when he woke, in the fetid stillness of the cabin, was the dust and fire and blood as the Russian tanks rolled into Budapest. His dreams were not of love, but only of hate.

When Nick shook him back to consciousness, he was dodging the guards on the Austrian border. It took him a few seconds to make the ten-thousand-mile journey to the Great Barrier Reef; then he yawned, kicked away the cockroaches that had been nibbling at his toes and heaved himself out of his bunk.

Breakfast, of course, was the same as always—rice, turtle eggs and bully beef, washed down with strong sweet tea. The best that could be said of Joey's cooking was that there was plenty of it. Tibor was used to the monotonous diet; he made up for it, and for other deprivations, when he was back on the mainland.

The sun had barely cleared the horizon when the dishes were stacked in the tiny galley and the lugger got under way.

Nick sounded cheerful as he took the wheel and headed out
from the island; the old pearling-master had every right to
be, for the patch of shell they were working was the richest
that Tibor had ever seen. With any luck, they would fill their
hold in another day or two, and sail back to T. I. with half a
ton of shell on board. And then, with a little more luck, he
could give up this stinking, dangerous job and get back to
civilization. Not that he regretted anything; the Greek had
treated him well, and he'd found some good stones when the
shells were opened. But he understood now, after nine
months on the Reef, why the number of white divers could
be counted on the fingers of one hand. Japs and Kanakas
and Islanders could take it—but damn few Europeans.

The diesel coughed into silence, and the *Arafura* coasted to
rest. They were some two miles from the island, which lay
low and green on the water, yet sharply divided from it by
its narrow band of dazzling beach. It was no more than a
nameless sand bar that a tiny forest had managed to capture,
and its only inhabitants were the myriads of stupid mutton-
birds that riddled the soft ground with their burrows and
made the night hideous with their banshee cries.

There was little talk as the three divers dressed; each man
knew what to do, and wasted no time in doing it. As Tibor
buttoned on his thick twill jacket, Blanco, his tender, rinsed
out the faceplate with vinegar so that it would not become
fogged. Then Tibor clambered down the rope ladder, while
the heavy helmet and lead corselet were placed over his
head. Apart from the jacket, whose padding spread the
weight evenly over his shoulders, he was wearing his ordinary clothes. In these warm waters there was no need for
rubber suits, and the helmet simply acted as a tiny diving
bell held in position by its weight alone. In an emergency the
wearer could—if he was lucky—duck out of it and swim back
to the surface unhampered. Tibor had seen this done, but
he had no wish to try the experiment for himself.

Each time he stood on the last rung of the ladder, gripping his shell bag with one hand and his safety line with the other, the same thought flashed through Tibor's mind. He was leaving the world he knew—but was it for an hour or was it forever? Down there on the sea bed was wealth and death, and one could be sure of neither. The chances were that this would be another day of uneventful drudgery, as were most of the days in the pearl diver's unglamorous life. But Tibor had seen one of his mates die, when his air hose tangled in the *Arafura*'s prop—and he had watched the agony of another whose body twisted with the bends. In the sea, nothing was ever safe or certain. You took your chances with open eyes—and if you lost, there was no point in whining.

He stepped back from the ladder, and the world of sun and sky ceased to exist. Top-heavy with the weight of his helmet, he had to backpedal furiously to keep his body upright. He could see nothing but a featureless blue mist as he sank towards the bottom, and he hoped that Blanco would not play out the safety line too quickly. Swallowing and snorting, he tried to clear his ears as the pressure mounted; the right one 'popped' quickly enough, but a piercing, intolerable pain grew rapidly in the left, which had bothered him for several days. He forced his hand up under the helmet, gripped his nose, and blew with all his might. There was an abrupt, soundless explosion somewhere inside his head, and the pain vanished instantly. He'd have no more trouble on this dive.

Tibor felt the bottom before he saw it. Since he was unable to bend over lest he risk flooding the open helmet, his vision in the downward direction was very limited. He could see around, but not immediately below. What he did see was reassuring in its drab monotony—gently undulating, muddy plain that faded out of sight about ten feet ahead. A yard to his left a tiny fish was nibbling at a piece of coral the size and shape of a lady's fan. That was all; there was no beauty, no underwater fairyland here. But there was money, and that was what mattered.

The safety line gave a gentle pull as the lugger started to drift downward, moving broadside-on across the patch, and Tibor began to walk forward with the springy, slow-motion step forced on him by weightlessness and water resistance. As Number Two diver he was working from the bow; amidships was Stephen, still comparatively inexperienced, while at the stern was the head diver, Billy. The three men seldom saw each other while they were working; each had his own lane to search as the *Arafura* drifted silently before the wind. Only at the extremes of the zigzags might they sometimes glimpse one another as dim shapes looming through the mist.

It needed a trained eye to spot the shells beneath their camouflage of algae and weeds, but often the molluscs betrayed themselves. When they felt the vibrations of the approaching diver, they would snap shut—and there would be a momentary, nacreous flicker in the gloom. Yet even then they sometimes escaped, for the moving ship might drag the diver past before he could collect the prize just out of reach. In the early days of his apprenticeship, Tibor had missed quite a few of the big silver lips—any one of which might have contained some fabulous pearl. Or so he had imagined, before the glamour of the profession had worn off, and he realized that pearls were so rare that you might as well forget them. The most valuable stone he'd ever brought up had been sold for fifty-six dollars, and the shell he gathered on a good morning was worth more than that. If the industry had depended on gems instead of mother-of-pearl, it would have gone broke years ago.

There was no sense of time in this world of mist. You walked beneath the invisible, drifting ship, with the throb of the air compressor pounding in your ears, the green haze moving past your eyes. At long intervals you would spot a shell, wrench it from the sea bed, and drop it in your bag. If you were lucky, you might gather a couple of dozen on a single drift across the patch; on the other hand, you might not find a single one.

You were alert for danger, but not worried by it. The real risks were simple, unspectacular things like tangled air hoses or safety lines—not sharks, groupers or octopuses. Sharks ran when they saw your air bubbles, and in all his hours of diving Tibor had seen just one octopus, every bit of two feet across. As for groupers—well, *they* were to be taken seriously, for they could swallow a diver at one gulp it they felt hungry enough. But there was little chance of meeting them on this flat and desolate plain; there was none of the coral caves in which they could make their homes.

The shock would not have been so great, therefore, if this uniform, level greyness had not lulled him into a sense of security. At one moment he was walking steadily towards an unreachable wall of mist, which retreated as fast as he approached. And then without warning, his private nightmare was looming above him.

Tibor hated spiders, and there was a certain creature in the sea that seemed deliberately contrived to take advantage of that phobia. He had never met one, and his mind had always shied away from the thought of such an encounter, but Tibor knew that the Japanese spider crab can span twelve feet across its spindly legs. That it was harmless mattered not in the least; a spider as big as a man simply had no right to exist.

As soon as he saw that cage of slender, joined limbs emerge from the all-encompassing greyness, Tibor began to scream with uncontrollable terror. He never remembered jerking his safety line, but Blanco reacted with the instantaneous perception of the ideal tender. His helmet still echoing to his screams, Tibor felt himself snatched from the sea bed, lifted towards light and air—and sanity. As he swept upwards, he saw both the strangeness and the absurdity of his mistake, and regained a measure of control. But he was still trembling so violently when Blanco lifted off his helmet that it was some time before he could speak.

'What the hell's going on here?' demanded Nick. 'Everyone knocking off work early?'

It was then that Tibor realized that he was not the first to come up. Stephen was sitting amidships, smoking a cigarette and looking completely unconcerned. The stern diver, doubtless wondering what had happened, was being hauled up willy-nilly by his tender, since the *Arafura* had come to rest and all operations had been suspended until the trouble was resolved.

'There's some kind of wreck down there,' said Tibor. 'I ran right into it. All I could see were a lot of wires and rods.'

To his annoyance and self-contempt, the memory set him trembling again.

'Don't see why *that* should give you the shakes,' grumbled Nick. Nor could Tibor; here on this sun-drenched deck, it was impossible to explain how a harmless shape glimpsed through the mist could set one's whole mind jangling with terror.

'I nearly got hung up on it,' he lied. 'Blanco pulled me clear just in time.'

'Hmm,' said Nick, obviously not convinced. 'Anyway, it ain't a ship.' He gestured towards the midships diver. 'Steve ran into a mess of ropes and cloth—like thick nylon, he says. Sounds like some kind of parachute.' The old Greek stared in disgust at the soggy stump of his cigar, then flicked it overboard. 'Soon as Billy's up, we'll go back and take a look. Might be worth something—remember what happened to Jo Chambers.'

Tibor remembered; the story was famous the whole length of the Great Barrier Reef. Jo had been a lone-wolf fisher-

man who in the last months of the war had spotted a DC-3
lying in shallow water a few miles off the Queensland coast.
After prodigies of singlehanded salvage, he had broken into
the fuselage and started unloading boxes of taps and dies,
perfectly protected by their greased wrappings. For a while
he had run a flourishing import business, but when the
police caught up with him he reluctantly revealed his source
of supply; Australian cops can be very persuasive.

And it was then, after weeks and weeks of backbreaking
underwater work, that Jo discovered what his DC-3 had been
carrying besides the miserable few hundred quid's worth of
tools he had been flogging to garages and workshops on the
mainland. The big wooden crates he'd never got round to
opening held a week's payroll for the U.S. Pacific forces
—most of it in twenty-dollar gold pieces.

No such luck here, thought Tibor as he sank over the side
again; but the aircraft—or whatever it was—might contain
valuable instruments, and there could be a reward for its
discovery. Besides, he owed it to himself; he wanted to see
exactly what it was that had given him such a fright.

Ten minutes later, he knew it was no aircraft. It was the
wrong shape and it was much too small—only about twenty
feet long and half that in width. Here and there on the
gently tapering body were access hatches and tiny ports
through which unknown instruments peered at the world. It
seemed unharmed, though one end had been fused as if by
terrific heat. From the other sprouted a tangle of antennas,
all of them broken or bent by the impact with the water.
Even now they bore an incredible resemblance to the legs of
a giant insect.

Tibor was no fool; he guessed at once what the thing was.
Only one problem remained, and he solved that with little
difficulty. Though they had been partly charred away by
heat, stencilled words could still be read on some of the
hatch covers. The letters were Cyrillic, and Tibor knew

enough Russian to pick out references to electrical supplies
and pressurizing systems.

'So they've lost a sputnik,' he told himself with satisfaction.
He could imagine what had happened; the thing had come
down too fast, and in the wrong place. Around one end
were the tattered remnants of flotation bags; they had burst
under the impact, and the vehicle had sunk like a stone. The
Arafura's crew would have to apologize to Joey; he hadn't
been drinking grog. What he'd seen burning across the stars
must have been the rocket carrier, separated from its pay
load and falling back unchecked into the Earth's atmosphere.

For a long time Tibor hovered on the sea bed, knees bent
in the diver's crouch as he regarded this space creature now
trapped in an alien element. His mind was full of half-
formed plans but none had yet come clearly into focus. He
no longer cared about the salvage money; much more important were the prospects of revenge. Here was one of the
proudest creations of Soviet technology—and Szabo Tibor,
late of Budapest, was the only man on earth who knew.

There must be some way of exploiting the situation—of
doing harm to the country and the cause he now hated with
such smouldering intensity. In his waking hours, he was seldom conscious of the hate, and still less did he ever stop to
analyse its real cause. Here in this lonely world of sea and
sky, of steaming mangrove swamps and dazzling coral
strands, there was nothing to recall the past. Yet he could
never escape it, and sometimes the demons in his mind
would awake, lashing him into a fury of rage or vicious, wan-
ton destructiveness. So far he had been lucky; he had not
killed anyone. But some day . . .

An anxious jerk from Blanco interrupted his reveries of
vengeance. He gave a reassuring signal to his tender, and
started a closer examination of the capsule. What did it
weigh? Could it be hoisted easily? There were many things

he had to discover, before he could settle on any definite plans.

He braced himself against the corrugated metal wall, and pushed cautiously. There was a definite movement as the capsule rocked on the sea bed. Maybe it could be lifted, even with the few pieces of tackle that the *Arafura* could muster. It was probably lighter than it looked.

Tibor pressed his helmet against a flat section of the hull and listened intently. He had half expected to hear some mechanical noise, such as the whirring of electric motors. Instead, there was utter silence. With the hilt of his knife, he rapped sharply on the metal, trying to gauge its thickness and to locate any weak spots. On the third try, he got results: but they were not what he had anticipated.

In a furious, desperate tattoo, the capsule rapped back at him.

Until this moment, Tibor had never dreamed that there might be someone inside; the capsule had seemed far too small. Then he realized that he had been thinking in terms of conventional aircraft; there was plenty of room here for a little pressure cabin in which a dedicated astronaut could spend a few cramped hours.

As a kaleidoscope can change its pattern completely in a single moment, so the half-formed plans in Tibor's mind dissolved and then crystallized into a new shape. Behind the thick glass of his helmet, he ran his tongue lightly across his lips. If Nick could have seen him now, he would have wondered—as he had sometimes done before—whether his Number Two diver was wholly sane. Gone were all thoughts of a remote and impersonal vengeance against something as abstract as a nation or a machine; now it would be man to man.

'Took your time, didn't you?' said Nick. 'What did you find?'

'It's Russian,' said Tibor. 'Some kind of sputnik. If we can get a rope around it, I think we can lift it off the bottom. But it's too heavy to get aboard.'

Nick chewed thoughtfully on his eternal cigar. The pearling master was worried about a point that had not occurred to Tibor. If there were any salvage operations around here, everyone would know where the *Arafura* had been drifting. When the news got back to Thursday Island, his private patch of shell would be cleaned out in no time.

They'd have to keep quiet about the whole affair, or else haul the damn thing up themselves and not say where they'd found it. Whatever happened, it looked like being more of a nuisance than it was worth. Nick, who shared most Australians' profound suspicion of authority, had already decided that all he'd get for his trouble would be a nice letter of thanks.

'The boys won't go down,' he said. 'They think it's a bomb. Want to leave it alone.'

'Tell 'em not to worry,' replied Tibor. 'I'll handle it.' He tried to keep his voice normal and unemotional but this was too good to be true. If the other divers heard the tapping from the capsule, his plans would have been frustrated.

He gestured to the island, green and lovely on the skyline.

'Only one thing we can do. If we can heave it a couple of feet off the bottom, we can run for the shore. Once we're in shallow water, it won't be too hard to haul it up on the beach. We can use the boats, and maybe get a block and tackle on one of those trees.'

Nick considered the idea without much enthusiasm. He doubted if they could get the sputnik through the reef, even on the leeward side of the island, but he was all in favour of lugging it away from this patch of shell; they could always dump it somewhere else, buoy the place, and still get whatever credit was going.

'O.K.,' he said. 'Down you go. That two-inch rope's the

strongest we've got—better take that. Don't be all the bloody day; we've lost enough time already.'

Tibor had no intention of being all day. Six hours would be quite long enough. That was one of the first things he had learned, from the signals through the wall.

It was a pity that he could not hear the Russian's voice; but the Russian could hear him, and that was what really mattered. When he pressed his helmet against the metal and shouted, most of his words got through. So far, it had been a friendly conversation; Tibor had no intention of showing his hand until the right psychological moment.

The first move had been to establish a code—one knock for 'yes', two for 'no'. After that, it was merely a matter of framing suitable questions; given time, there was no fact or idea that could not be communicated by means of these two signals. It would have been a much tougher job if Tibor had been forced to use his indifferent Russian; he had been pleased, but not surprised, to find that the trapped pilot understood English perfectly.

There was air in the capsule for another five hours; the occupant was uninjured; yes, the Russians knew where it had come down. The last reply gave Tibor pause. Perhaps the pilot was lying, but it might very well be true. Although something had obviously gone wrong with the planned return to Earth, the tracking ships out in the Pacific must have located the impact point—with what accuracy, he could not guess. Still, did that matter? It might take them days to get here, even if they came racing straight into Australian territorial waters without bothering to get permission from Canberra. He was master of the situation; the entire might of the U.S.S.R. could do nothing to interfere with his plans—until it was much too late.

The heavy rope fell in coils on the sea bed, stirring up a cloud of silt that drifted like smoke down the slow current. Now that the sun was higher in the sky, the underwater world was no longer wrapped in a grey, twilight gloom. The sea bed was colourless but bright, and the boundary of vision was now almost fifteen feet away. For the first time, Tibor could see the space capsule in its entirety. It was such a peculiar-looking object, being designed for conditions beyond all normal experience, that there was an eye-teasing wrongness about it. One searched in vain for a front or a rear; there was no way of telling in what direction it pointed as it sped along its orbit.

Tibor pressed his helmet against the metal and shouted.

'I'm back,' he called. 'Can you hear me?'

Tap

'I've got a rope, and I'm going to tie it on to the parachute cables. We're about three kilometres from an island, and as soon as we've made you fast we'll head towards it. We can't lift you out of the water with the gear on the lugger, so we'll try to get you up on the beach. You understand?'

Tap

It took only a few moments to secure the rope; now he had better get clear before the *Arafura* started to lift. But there was something he had to do first.

'Hello!' he shouted. 'I've fixed the rope. We'll lift in a minute. D'you hear me?'

Tap

'Then you can hear this too. You'll never get there alive. I've fixed *that* as well.'

Tap, tap

'You've got five hours to die. My brother took longer than that, when he ran into your mine field. You understand? I'm from Budapest. I hate you and your country and everything it stands for. You've taken my home, my family, made my people slaves. I wish I could see your face now—I wish I could watch you die, as I had to watch Theo. When you're halfway to the island, this rope is going to break where I cut it, I'll go down and fix another—and that'll break, too. You can sit in there and wait for the bumps.'

Tibor stopped abruptly, shaken and exhausted by the violence of his emotion. There was no room for logic or reason
in this orgasm of hate; he did not pause to think, for he
dared not. Yet somewhere far down inside his mind the real
truth was burning its way up towards the light of consciousness.

It was not the Russians he hated, for all that they had
done. It was himself, for he had done more. The blood of
Theo, and of ten thousand countrymen, was upon his own
hands. No one could have been a better Communist than he
had been, or have more supinely believed the propaganda
from Moscow. At school and college, he had been the first to
hunt out and denounce 'traitors'. (How many had he sent to
the labour camps or the AVO torture chambers?) When he
had seen the truth, it was far, far too late; and even then, he
had not fought—he had run.

He had run across the world, trying to escape his guilt;
and the two drugs of danger and dissipation had helped him
to forget the past. The only pleasures life gave him now
were the loveless embraces he sought so feverishly when he
was on the mainland, and his present mode of existence was
proof that these were not enough. If he now had the power
to deal out death, it was only because he had come here in
search of it himself.

There was no sound from the capsule; its silence seemed
contemptuous, mocking. Angrily, Tibor banged against it
with the hilt of his knife.

'Did you hear me?' he shouted. 'Did you hear me?'

No answer.

'Damn you! I know you're listening! If you don't answer,
I'll hole you and let the water in!'

He was sure that he could, with the sharp point of his
knife. But that was the last thing he wanted to do; that
would be too quick, too easy an ending.

There was still no sound; maybe the Russian had fainted.
Tibor hoped not, but there was no point in waiting any

longer. He gave a vicious parting bang on the capsule, and signalled to his tender.

Nick had news for him when he broke the surface.

'T. I. radio's been squawking,' he said. 'The Ruskies are asking everyone to look out for one of their rockets. They say it should be floating somewhere off the Queensland coast. Sounds as if they want it badly.'

'Did they say anything else about it?' Tibor asked anxiously.

'Oh yes—it's been round the moon a couple of times.'

'That all?'

'Nothing else that I remember. There was a lot of science stuff I didn't get.'

That figured; it was just like the Russians to keep as quiet as they could about an experiment that had gone wrong.

'You tell T. I. that we'd found it?'

'Are you crazy? Anyway, the radio's crook; couldn't if we wanted to. Fixed that rope properly?'

'Yes—see if you can haul her off the bottom.'

The end of the rope had been wound round the mainmast, and in a few seconds it had been drawn taut. Although the sea was calm, there was a slight swell, and the lugger was rolling ten or fifteen degrees. With each roll, the gunwales would rise a couple of feet, then drop again. There was a lift here of several tons, but one had to be careful in using it.

The rope twanged, the woodwork groaned and creaked, and for a moment Tibor was afraid that the weakened line would part too soon. But it held, and the load lifted. They got a further hoist on the second roll—and on the third. Then the capsule was clear of the sea bed, and the *Arafura* was listing slightly to port.

'Let's go,' said Nick, taking the wheel. 'Should be able to get her half a mile before she bumps again.'

The lugger began to move slowly towards the island, carrying its hidden burden beneath it. As he leaned on the rails, letting the sun steam the moisture from his sodden clothing, Tibor felt at peace for the first time in—how many months? Even his hate had ceased to burn like fire in his brain. Perhaps, like love, it was a passion that could never be satisfied; but for the moment, at least, it was satiated.

There was no weakening of his resolve; he was implacably set upon the vengeance that had been so strangely—so miraculously—placed within his power. Blood called for blood, and now the ghosts that haunted him might rest at last. Yet he felt a strange sympathy, even pity, towards the unknown man through whom he could now strike back at the enemies who had once been his friends. He was robbing them of much more than a single life—for what was one man, even a highly trained scientist—to the Russians? What he was taking from them was power and prestige and knowledge, the things they valued most.

He began to worry when they were two thirds of the way to the island, and the rope had not parted. There were still four hours to go, and that was much too long. For the first time it occurred to him that his entire plan might miscarry, and might even recoil on his head. Suppose that, despite everything, Nick managed to get the capsule up on the beach before the deadline?

With a deep 'twang' that set the whole ship vibrating, the rope came snaking out of the water, scattering spray in all directions.

'Might have guessed,' muttered Nick. 'She was just starting to bump. You like to go down again, or shall I send one of the boys?'

'I'll take it,' Tibor hastily answered. 'I can do it quicker than they can.'

That was perfectly true, but it took him twenty minutes to locate the capsule. The *Arafura* had drifted well away from it before Nick could stop the engine, and there was a time when Tibor wondered if he would ever find it again. He quartered the sea bed in great arcs, and it was not until he had accidentally tangled in the trailing parachute that his search was ended. The shrouds lay pulsating slowly in the current like some weird and hideous marine monster—but there was nothing Tibor feared now except frustration, and his pulse barely quickened as he saw the whitely looming mass ahead.

The capsule was scratched and stained with mud, but appeared undamaged. It was lying on its side now, looking rather like a giant milk churn that had been tipped over. The passenger must have been bumped around, but if he'd fallen all the way back from the moon, he must have been well padded and was probably still in good shape. Tibor hoped so; it would be a pity if the remaining three hours were wasted.

Once again he rested the verdigrised copper of his helmet against the no-longer-quite-so-brightly-gleaming metal of the capsule.

'Hello!' he shouted. 'Can you hear me?'

Perhaps the Russian would try to balk him by remaining silent—but that, surely, was asking too much of any man's self-control. Tibor was right; almost at once there was the sharp knock of the reply.

'So glad you're there,' he called back. 'Things are working out just the way I said, though I guess I'll have to cut the rope a little deeper.'

The capsule did not answer. It never answered again, though Tibor banged and banged on the next dive—and on the next. But he hardly expected it to then, for they'd had to stop for a couple of hours to ride out a squall, and the time limit had expired long before he made his final descent. He was a little annoyed about that, for he had planned a farewell message. He shouted it just the same, though he knew he was wasting his breath.

By early afternoon, the *Arafura* had come in as close as she dared. There were only a few feet of water beneath her, and the tide was falling. The capsule broke surface at the bottom of each trough, and was now firmly stranded on a sandbank. There was no hope of moving it any farther; it was stuck, until a high sea would dislodge it.

Nick regarded the situation with an expert eye.

'There's a six-foot tide tonight,' he said. 'The way she's lying now, she'll be in only a couple of feet of water at low. We'll be able to get at her with the boats.'

They waited off the sandbank while the sun and the tide went down, and the radio broadcast intermittent reports of a search that was coming closer but still far away. Late in the afternoon the capsule was almost clear of the water; the crew rowed the small boat towards it with a reluctance which Tibor, to his annoyance, found himself sharing.

'It's got a door in the side,' said Nick suddenly. 'Jeeze —think there's anyone in it?'

'Could be,' answered Tibor, his voice not as steady as he thought. Nick glanced at him curiously. His diver had been acting strangely all day, but he knew better than to ask him what was wrong. In this part of the world, you soon learned to mind your own business.

The boat, rocking slightly in the choppy sea, had now come alongside the capsule. Nick reached out and grabbed one of the twisted antenna stubs; then, with catlike agility, he clambered up the curved metal surface. Tibor made no attempt to follow him, but watched silently from the boat as he examined the entrance hatch.

'Unless it's jammed,' Nick muttered, 'there must be some way of opening it from outside. Just our luck if it needs special tools.'

His fears were groundless. The word 'Open' had been stencilled in ten languages around the recessed door catch, and it took only seconds to deduce its mode of operation. As the air hissed out, Nick said 'Phew!' and turned suddenly pale. He looked at Tibor as if seeking support, but Tibor avoided his eye. Then, reluctantly, Nick lowered himself into the capsule.

He was gone for a long time. At first, they could hear muffled bangings and bumpings from the inside, followed by a string of bilingual profanity. And then there was a silence that went on and on and on.

When at last Nick's head appeared above the hatchway, his leathery, wind-tanned face was grey and streaked with tears. As Tibor saw this incredible sight, he felt a sudden ghastly premonition. Something had gone horribly wrong, but his mind was too numb to anticipate the truth. It came soon enough, when Nick handed down his burden, no larger than an over-sized doll.

Blanco took it, as Tibor shrank to the stern of the boat. As he looked at the calm, waxen face, fingers of ice seemed to close not only upon his heart, but around his loins. In the same moment, both hate and desire died forever within him, as he knew the price of his revenge.

The dead astronaut was perhaps more beautiful in death than she had been in life; tiny though she was, she must have been tough as well as highly trained to qualify for this mission. As she lay at Tibor's feet, she was neither a Russian nor the first human being to have seen the far side of the moon; she was merely the girl that he had killed.

Nick was talking, from a long way off.

'She was carrying this,' he said, in an unsteady voice. 'Had it tight in her hand—took me a long time to get it out.'

Tibor scarcely heard him, and never even glanced at the tiny spool of tape lying in Nick's palm. He could not guess, in this moment beyond all feeling, that the Furies had yet to close in upon his soul—and that soon the whole world would be listening to an accusing voice from beyond the grave, branding him more irrevocably than any man since Cain.

Gideon and the Vintage Car Thefts

J. J. Marric (John Creasey)

One of the most common crimes in the city of London—in fact, in nearly all the big cities of the world—is car stealing. Many hundreds of cars are stolen every week in London, most of them new and of popular makes, so that they can be sold easily.

The car thieves, often working in highly organized gangs, have a number of tricks to help them get the "hot" cars off their hands. But these tricks are well known to the police. If the engine number of a car has been filed off, infra-red rays can still reveal this number; if the car has been resprayed, it is easy to check how long the cellulose has been dry, and what color is underneath. For every car thief's trick there is a police countermeasure.

All this was known, as second nature, to Commander George Gideon of the Criminal Investigation Department of New Scotland Yard. But Gideon seldom gave car thieves much thought, unless they reached a new high level, or unless they failed to fit into the normal pattern.

He was a big, powerful, rugged man, with iron-gray hair, and as he entered the N.E. Divisional Police Headquarters one hazy autumn morning, the boards groaning under his deliberate tread, every man sprang to attention.

This time it was the Divisional Superintendent who committed a crime. He kept George Gideon waiting. Everyone in the station was on edge about this, except Gideon himself, who stood by the Superintendent's window and looked out into the station yard. Standing among the police cars was an old black Bugatti, a vintage model, beautifully painted, all its brasswork polished and gleaming.

The Superintendent, a tall thin man, came in.

"Sorry, Commander. I've been down in the cells talking to a fellow who all but strangled his wife last night."

"How does he feel about it now?" asked Gideon.

The Superintendent grinned. "He says he'll never forgive himself for not having finished her off!"

"The longer he cools his heels the better," said Gideon. "Anything much in, otherwise?"

"No. What's brought you?"

"Just dropped in to keep you on your toes," said Gideon dryly. "What's that old crock doing in the yard?"

"We picked it up this morning. It was reported stolen six months ago. Remember?"

Gideon did not remember, but he did not say so. He could recall reading of the theft and recovery of other vintage motor cars, however, from wire-wheeled Bentleys to Model T Fords; but this particular series of crimes had been so insignificant that he had taken little notice of it. Now his mind began to roam.

"Get the thief?" he inquired.

"Not yet."

"Where was it found?"

"In an old warehouse near the docks. We were looking for that hijacked load of cigarettes taken from Hyne's Wharf last night, and doing a routine check of the places it might be."

"Who gave the car all that spit and polish?"

"Well, the owner obviously didn't—and *we* didn't—so I suppose it must have been the fellow who pinched it."

"Bit peculiar," said Gideon thoughtfully. "I'd like to have a look in the warehouse. Can you spare the time?"

"For you, yes. For anyone else I'm working too hard as it is."

"Poor old chap," scoffed Gideon.

Half an hour later the Commander was standing in the warehouse, gazing round at the high rafters, at the holes in the roof where slates had fallen through, at the high loading platform and the dusty floor. As the sun's rays filtered through the long window, lighting that corner of the warehouse where the vintage car had been found, his keen gaze fell on some pale flecks of congealed liquid. He bent down, touched one, and sniffed at his finger.

"Metal polish," he remarked.

"Yes, the thief worked on it all right, and he worked on it here," the Superintendent said. "Come and see this."

Gideon followed him to the loading section where the Superintendent leaned over a big cardboard box which contained polishing cloths, a jam jar with several paint brushes, a tin of black enamel paint, a cleaning powder, and various odd bottles and cans.

"We must try these for fingerprints," said Gideon. "Any prints on the car?"

"Plenty, but we haven't got any of them in Records."

"What have you done about it?"

"Sent a report—Colonel Riordan, the owner, is due to come and identify his property sometime today. But why are you so interested, Commander? It's a straightforward job. These old cars are worth a lot of money; they're kept in museums and private collections all over the country, and the more spit and polish the more valuable they are. It's as simple as that."

"Hmm," grunted Gideon. "Ask the owner if he could spare time to come and see me at the Yard, will you?"

"Don't tell me you see some major crime lurking behind this," said the Superintendent. "It's just a new form of the old game." When Gideon didn't respond he went on, "I'll give Colonel Riordan your message."

At half-past three that afternoon the old and tired building of New Scotland Yard was brightened by a boisterous, even flamboyant individual in a loud tweed suit and R.A.C. Veteran's tie.

"My name's Riordan, Colonel Riordan," he boomed in the hushed hall. "I believe you have a Commander Gideon here. He wants to see me."

Very soon Colonel Riordan had boomed his way into Gideon's office.

"Want to say thank you. Wonderful chaps, you police. Didn't think I'd ever see that car again. Congratulations. How much do I have to pay?"

"Pay for what?" asked Gideon, a little overwhelmed.

"Reward, sir, reward! For getting the car back."

"You settle that when you pay your taxes," Gideon said. "Have you heard about the other old cars that have been stolen recently?"

"I certainly have!"

"Do you collect vintage cars?" asked Gideon.

"Have for years. Some people collect stamps, some collect jade, some collect paperweights. I collect old cars. Got fifty-three of them. Keep them on show mostly, but I always like to drive a different one each week. Shock of my life when this one disappeared."

"Have you had any others stolen?"

"Any *others?*" Colonel Riordan looked alarmed.

"Have you bought any of the stolen ones?" asked Gideon, with deceptive mildness.

Colonel Riordan gaped. "*Bought* them? Stolen cars? Good God, Commander, you must be mad!"

Gideon raised a soothing hand. "Can you think of any car collector who would buy a car, knowing it to be stolen?"

Colonel Riordan's eyes gleamed with excitement. He leaned forward. "I *see*. Like an art lover might buy a stolen painting, you mean. Buy it, knowing that he would have to keep it hidden, and that only he could enjoy it. Well, such connoisseurs may exist, but not in this line of business, Commander. The whole fun of owning an old crock is showing it off to the other fellow. There's no undercover buying in the vintage-car market, you can take it from me."

"If you're quite sure—"

"Take it from me," repeated Colonel Riordan. "It's like an exclusive club, Commander. If anyone pinches a car of mine, all the others in the game feel as if they've lost a car, too. There aren't any exceptions. And I know every owner, Commander, every collector."

"Who cleans and polishes these old cars?" asked Gideon.

"The owners, as likely as not—or their mechanics. But owner or mechanic, they all have the same sense of pride in looking after these antique cars. They treat them as if they were living creatures, and that's the truth of it. Cleaning and polishing is a labor of love."

Again Gideon looked deceptively innocent. "And what do you think of the condition of your Bugatti, Colonel?"

"Never seen it better!"

"A labor of love, perhaps," said Gideon softly.

"Absolutely, Commander! No doubt about it. A great deal of elbow grease and loving care went into maintaining the appearance of that car."

"So the thief must also have that sense of pride you were telling me about," murmured Gideon.

"What's that? Oh!" Colonel Riordan looked thoughtful. "I see what you mean. Couldn't have been stolen for resale and certainly couldn't have been driven about by the thief—he had to hide it somewhere and keep it to himself, by Jove! Undercover—just the kind of man I said we didn't have in the old crocks game. You've made your point!"

"There have been nine cases of vintage cars having been stolen," began Gideon, "and—"

"Everyone's recovered in first-class condition!"

"That is so," agreed Gideon. "Now, no one who could afford to buy them would be likely to steal them, would they?"

"Deuced unlikely," Colonel Riordan agreed.

"And according to the reports no two have been stolen in the same period. So, assuming all of them were taken by the same person, the thief steals one, hides it, and takes care of it. Only after it has been recovered by the police does he steal another. So it looks as if his only object is to have a car—*any* car, providing it's vintage—that he can care for."

"Like these women who steal other women's babies!"

"Well, perhaps," agreed Gideon. "So we're looking for a man who loves vintage cars but can't afford to buy them."

Colonel Riordan was staring at him intently.

"Do you know of such a man?" asked Gideon flatly.

There was a few moments' pause.

"No," said the Colonel sharply. "No, sir, I do not."

He rose from his chair, as if suddenly anxious to leave.

"I'll be grateful if you'll let me know whether you hear of one," Gideon remarked. "He'll probably be the man we want."

"Yes, yes," said Colonel Riordan, almost impatiently. "I'll let you know, Commander."

"And one of these days I'd like to look over your collection," said Gideon, following him to the door.

The Colonel turned. "And so you shall, Commander, so you shall. I'll send you an invitation. Goodbye for now, sir. I hope you get your man."

But the police did not get their man, and in the next three months the investigation petered out, partly because of more urgent cases, partly because no more vintage cars were stolen. Early in the fourth month Gideon received an invitation to visit Colonel Riordan's Old Crock Museum, in a Surrey country town.

"And now for the moment of truth!" boomed Colonel Riordan, turning to Gideon after an excellent luncheon. "You are about to see the finest collection of old crocks in the western world!"

The collection certainly seemed to measure up to the Colonel's boast. Benz, Bentley, Hispano-Suiza, Duesenberg, there they were, vintage cars of all shapes, sizes, and makes. And each one shone. Brasswork, coachwork, chassis, wheels, engine, radiator, upholstery—outside and in, everything was bright and gleaming.

Acting as their guide was a man in his early forties whose eyes glowed, whose voice was eager, as he described the history, the virtues, of every car.

"Amazing chap," Colonel Riordan said to Gideon an hour later, as they walked back toward the house. "He's done practically all the work himself. Dotes on it. Bit peculiar in some ways, almost simple, you might say. But old crocks mean everything to him. I hired him as an odd-job man, actually—didn't trust him with the cars to start with, though he begged me to let him look after them. Used to polish most of them myself. But when I got the Bugatti back—and after our little talk, Commander"—Colonel Riordan paused, looking sharply at Gideon, who said nothing—"I let him take over completely. It's come off so far. Works his fingers to the bone."

"You're lucky to have such a man," Gideon said solemnly.

"I am indeed. By the way, Commander, did you ever catch the fellow we were talking about that day?"

There was a hint of laughter in the Colonel's eyes.

"No," said Gideon. "He's stopped operating. He's probably found the job he was looking for," he added mildly.

Look Out When I'm Mad

Corey Ford

I'll admit I can write a pretty forceful letter when I'm crossed. Actually I have to be careful not to make it *too* forceful, for fear the recipient will be so crushed by my sarcasm and biting wit that he'll slink out of town and enlist in the Foreign Legion under an assumed name. Sometimes I don't know my own strength.

Usually I start off with a sarcastic salutation like "My dear Neighbor." This is loaded with irony, of course, because my dear neighbor's three children have been playing Indians in my flower bed and have made off with my driveway sign to decorate their teepee. "Evidently you are not aware that the first obligation of a parent is to teach his offspring to respect the property of others." I feel this opening sentence sets a stern but dignified tone for the whole letter. "If you would devote your energies to the care and upbringing of your family, instead of spending your time watching television at all hours of the night" (a sly reference to the fact that my neighbor was running his TV set full blast at two o'clock this morning) "I should not be forced to call your attention to the fact that the sign at the end of my driveway has been removed for the third time this week. Very truly yours."

Satisfied, I seal the envelope and start out to the mailbox, only to run into my neighbor and his three children coming up the driveway. "Why, hello there," I smile, beaming indulgently as one of the tots uproots the post the sign was on and bangs me with it across the shins, "anything I can do for you, old man?"

"I just dropped over to borrow your TV set," the neighbor says. "Mine quit for some reason, and I got some people coming over to the house tonight."

Whereupon I go back inside again and try to pry the stamp off the envelope, so I can use it on the next letter of complaint I write.

It doesn't really make much difference whether I mail the letter or not. The other day at the office I dictated a rather stiff rebuke to a local workman who had promised a month ago to put up my storm windows. "My dear Mr. Muzzey," I began, biting off the words between my teeth, "evidently you are not aware that the first obligation of a workman is to keep his promise." I paused and glanced at my secretary, who was looking at me with obvious admiration. "The guiding principle in any employer-employee relationship is to honor a contract," I continued tersely, "particularly if the employee has already accepted a down payment of ten dollars ($10.00) to install my storm windows." The girl's expression seemed to say that here was a man who brooked no inefficiency among his subordinates, firm but always fair, and universally respected for his ability to command. "Evidently you are not aware——"

"You awreddy said that," my secretary pointed out.

"Did I?" I murmured, a little shaken. "Well, just end it 'Very truly yours' and sent it off right away."

A few days later Mr. Muzzey showed up at the house. "Say, I got your note about them storm windows," he said, "but the kids all been sick, and the truck's broke down, and my wife's got to go to the hospital again, and I was wondering could I get another advance of ten dollars?"

"Why, of course," I replied promptly, taking out my wallet, "and don't you worry about those windows, Mr. Muzzey. Any time before spring will do."

I'm pretty good at composing stern speeches at night after I've gone to bed. I'll lie awake by the hour, for instance, rehearsing what I'm going to say to Junior tomorrow morning when he asks to borrow the car for the high school dance. This is a difficult decision to make, but a stern parent must consider the boy's own good. Evidently Junior is not aware that the first obligation of a teen-ager is to acquire self-reliance. (This is always good for a start.) If he had occupied himself during the summer at some gainful pursuit, instead of sleeping until noon and then going swimming, he might be able to afford a car of his own by now. It is not that I wish to deny him the pleasure of driving his girl to the dance, I point out, but when I was his age I used to get up every morning at four and milk the cows (maybe I should change that to delivering the papers, in case Junior ever asks me how to milk a cow), and thus I learned the value of money. I am sorry to refuse this time, but perhaps this experience will teach him that a car is a very expensive property and should not be brought back with cigarette burns in the upholstery and the right front fender crumpled.

By the time I have gone over this speech several times in my mind, polishing it here and there and working out the right intonations, I can't go back to sleep the rest of the night, and I'm so tired at breakfast that I not only tell Junior he can have the car but also agree to let him borrow my tux. As a result I lie awake all the following night, waiting for him to bring the car back and find out if the *left* front fender is crumpled.

I am a master of the riposte when I engage in repartee with a surly traffic cop who has just bawled me out for some minor traffic violation. The trouble is that this repartee invariably takes place after the cop has finished bawling me out and I'm driving down the road alone, gripping the wheel and muttering to myself. Right at the start I throw the cop off guard by insisting that he bring me to the local magistrate at once. (This is a slight deviation from the facts, because what I actually said to the cop was: "I'm sorry, officer, you're perfectly right, I promise not to let it happen again.") I am arraigned before the judge, who is instantly aware that I am a cut or two above the average defendant, and who asks me respectfully: "How do you plead, sir?"

"I plead guilty, your honor."

"So you plead guilty, eh?" he repeats, a trifle nonplussed. "Just what do you plead guilty to?"

"I plead guilty to being an honest, law-abiding American citizen," I reply as the courtroom is suddenly hushed, "whose only crime, if you can call it that, was to focus his attention so thoroughly on the job of driving that he just happened to overlook one little traffic light which accidentally turned red." The judge glances uneasily at the chief of police and the mayor, who have evidently hurried over to the courtroom when they heard that a sensational case was coming up. "While I do not object to paying a just fine if your honor so orders, there's one question I should like to ask the court."

The judge bites his lip nervously. "What question is that, sir?"

"Do I look like a fathead?"

"No," says the judge. (I've never figured out what I'd do if he said yes.)

"Am I an imbecile? Am I a moron? Am I an inmate of a school for the feeble-minded?"

"Certainly not," says the judge. "Why do you ask?"

"Because that is what this man called me," I reply, glancing at the traffic cop beside me, who wilts perceptibly. "Evidently he is not aware that the first obligation of a policeman is to encourage respect for the law." The cop's lower lip is trembling, and he looks as if he's going to cry. "It is just such a surly attitude as this which breeds crime and delinquency in our fair land."

The judge reaches over the bench to shake my hand, followed in turn by the chief of police and the mayor, while the courtroom echoes to applause and shouts of "Hurrah!," accompanied by the loud wailing of a siren. For some reason the siren keeps getting louder, and I glance out the window of my car at a cop on a motorcycle who is waving his hand.

"Pull over, fathead," he orders as I stop. "You just went through two red lights, and you're weaving back and forth all over the road like a moron. You belong to a school for the feeble-minded or somepin?"

"I'm sorry, officer," I say hurriedly, "you're perfectly right, I promise not to let it happen again."

I'm really at my best, though, when I'm brushing my teeth in the morning. Not only is my mind as sharp as a tack at this early hour, but the snorting and whooshing sounds I make help to conceal the sound of my voice in case somebody is listening outside the bathroom door. There's no end to the brilliant successes I score this way, crumpling my opponent with sheer logic, or occasionally halting my toothbrush in its stride to deliver a particularly telling sally. I haven't lost an argument to my mirror yet.

Sometimes I lean over the wash basin in my pajamas,

scowling at my reflection in the glass, and demand to know why I am not worth another twenty-five dollars a month, Mr. Bessemer, particularly since everybody else in the office got a raise last week, and if you don't think my efforts merit this long overdue recognition, then I am quite prepared to submit my resignation at once. On other mornings I have it out with the waiter at lunch yesterday who charged me for an order of corned beef hash that he never brought, or the taxi driver who took me six blocks out of the way and then complained about my tip, or the plumber who didn't fix the hot-water faucet in the tub that kept dripping all night long. Occasionally when I am shaving the image in the mirror is my wife, who doesn't seem to realize that I'm tired out after working all day and the last thing I want to do is get all dolled up in a dinner coat tonight and take her to the Philhar-monic. "Evideddly," I say thickly, because my face is covered with lather, "you are dod aware dad de firds obbligashed of a wive——"

Unfortunately this is as far as I get, because along about this time my wife pokes her head in the door and suggests that I stop talking to myself and finish shaving, George, or we'll be late to the concert.

In short, there are no limits to my formidable temper when aroused. The other night we were just sitting down to dinner when the doorbell rang, and my wife reported that a member of the local fire department was selling tickets to the annual Fireman's Ball. "This is nothing but a legalized hold-up," I said, slamming my fist on the table. "I pay my taxes, and I resent being shaken down for an added contribution. Every year I've bought two tickets, but this year I draw the line." My wife started to protest, but I silenced her with a gesture. "The time has come," I announced firmly, striding toward the door, "to give this fellow a piece of my mind."

By the way, do you know anybody who'd like a couple of extra tickets to the annual Fireman's ball?

Jet-Propelled Turban

S. J. Perelman

If travel has taught me nothing more, and it certainly has, it's this: you never know when some trifling incident, utterly without significance, may pitchfork you into adventure or, by the same token, may not. A look across a smoky room, a chance word or gesture, and all of a sudden you're standing breathless before a bead curtain in Cairo or clinging to an outrigger in the Nicobars or pawning your cuff links at Simpson's. I for one never dreamed as I stooped to retrieve a hairbrush from under the washbowl of a Paris hotel room last December that I was taking the first step in a grotesque excursion across the Indian Ocean with that venerable mainspring, His Highness Seyyid Sir Khalifa bin Harub, the Sultan of Zanzibar. Could I have foreseen the complications in the offing, I probably would have brushed my hair with a toothbrush and let it go hang. But then, the toothbrush was under the basin, too. I'd had a couple of pousse-cafés the night before.

What happened was simple to the point of banality. After ineffectually groping around under the sink, I miscalculated the amount of headroom over me and laid open my scalp as though it had been cleft by a yataghan. A pharmacist in the Rue de Vaugirard, absorbed in bottling leeches and obviously a figment of René Clair's imagination, paused long enough to patch me up grudgingly, and I went into a *brasserie* hard by for a restorative. There, staring meditatively across the zinc into the *patronne's* blouse, was an English sculptor named Noel Desuetude, who recognized me at once as an old companion of his Montparnasse days. Under other circumstances, I could have given the man an argument, but it was folly to be knocked down in my weakened condition, and I humored him. When he started reaching for the menu, however, I played my ace.

"Kenya?" he said, crestfallen. "You mean you're flying there this very noon? Damn it, I'd rather counted on your buying me lunch. Ah, well, another time. See here, though, you really must look up my godfather in Nairobi. He's the head of East African Airways—hellishly influential cove."

"Gladly," I said. "Jot down his name, will you?"

"I don't know it, to be candid," he said. "The fact is he's not my godfather at all, but we English are a clannish lot. I mean we're slow to make friends, but once we warm up, we can't do enough for you. Like, for instance, the way I'm sending you on to my godfather in Nairobi."

"Yes, and I'm deeply obliged—" I began.

"Now, don't start slobbering over me like a confounded sheepdog," he said testily. "If you must show your gratitude, pay for these." He shoved a pile of saucers toward me. "Sorry to bolt, but I'm meeting a popsy the other side of Paris. *A bientôt.*"

Well, around a month later, at a supper party in Muthaiga, a residential quarter of Nairobi, I met a well-set-up chap named Sorsbie, keen as mustard—there was some on the tablecloth, so one could judge—who proved to be the head of East African Airways. Seizing an opportune moment when the conversation had turned on bogus godsons, I told him about my encounter. Though he pretended to be deaf, as your Englishman frequently will out of shyness, I could see he was engrossed.

"And you paid his score, did you?" he asked. "You know, you ought to have your head examined."

"I did, but they couldn't find anything," I said. "If there was porcelain in the brain, wouldn't I feel it?"

"Only time will tell," he said darkly. "These things take a while to show. I say," he went on, with a thoughtful frown, "in a way I feel morally responsible for what this sponge in Paris did to you, and I'd like to make amends. Ever hear of the island of Pemba?"

"Gee, I can't use any more real estate," I protested. "I've got a farm in Pennsylvania—"

"It's about thirty miles northeast of Zanzibar," said Sorsbie, rolling over me like a Juggernaut, "and part of the Sultan's domain. We're opening an airfield there day after tomorrow, and we're flying over the Sultan and some other bigwigs in a special plane to dedicate it. Why don't you come along, too? Fascinating old duffer, His Highness. You two should have lots in common."

Offhand, I couldn't guess what it might be, outside inordinate wealth, but Sorsbie's heart was set on our meeting and I acceded. Late the next afternoon, I flew to Zanzibar, where the junket was to originate, and, boarding an ancient tumbril at the airport, set off through the labyrinthine alleys of the town for the hotel. In the car was another bird of passage off the same flight, a corpulent, dynamic gentleman in white sharkskin, whose artificial choppers sparkled with veritable ingots of gold. His languishing sidelong glances told me he was perishing to make friends. The opportunity came when he saw me extract a packet of Bisodol tablets.

"An American!" he said delightedly. "From your aristocratic nose, I thought you were a Portuguese hidalgo. Permit me, sir," he went on, deftly plucking a tablet from my hand. "I never miss a chance to eat these when they are offered. You know, we Greeks are authorities on heartburn —heartburn and women, ha ha ha. If you please—my card."

I took it and learned that fate had thrown me with Constantine Tigris, domiciled at Arusha, Tanganyika, and styling himself an industrialist. He seemed so hurt at my inability to produce a card that I brought out my passport, which he studied with deep interest, nodding repeatedly, and then thrust into his breast pocket.

"Would you mind awfully returning that?" I asked hesitantly. "It isn't the intrinsic cost, but it's got sentimental associations—"

"Oh—oh! Forgive me, my dear fellow," he said, overcome with chagrin. "Imagine being so absent-minded. There you are. By the way, if you want to sell this at any time, I pay cash and no questions asked."

I promised not to dispose of it without giving him priority, and, secreting it under my toupee, withdrew into a marmoreal silence. As we were both registering at the hotel, though, the clerk gave me a verbal message that Bikinized Mr. Hubris. It appeared that a seneschal wearing a dolman and a gold hearing aid had left word requesting me to join the Sultan's party at eight the next morning at the airport. Mr. Tigris's jaw dropped, and he watched me ascend the stairs as if I were clothed in white samite. Throughout the dinner, he kept observing me furtively from his table, and afterward pursued me into the lobby and insisted on standing me to a brandy.

"Why didn't you say you were a diplomat?" he reproached me. "I had no idea you were a friend of the Sultan—"

I cut him short and, without demeaning myself unnecessarily, explained I had no official status at the forthcoming exercises on Pemba. An indulgent smile clearly revealed his disbelief. Typical American modesty, chuckled Mr. Tigris, signaling the waiter to replenish my glass; he was certain I was the emissary of persons of the highest consequence in Washington, that grave decisions would stem from my visit. Then, with mastodonlike subtlety, he maneuvered around to the gimmick. A little group of philanthropists he knew was interested in establishing a casino in Zanzibar—a place where the natives could eat ices and enjoy classical music and, if they felt disposed, dally with a harmless game of stuss. If I could drop a word *en passant* into the Sultan's ear, the syndicate would be overjoyed to set aside a few shares of stock for both of us. . . .

There being no exact local equivalent for the word "shill," it took ten minutes and considerable vehemence to disabuse Mr. Tigris. He was pained at my obduracy but not daunted. Waylaying me at breakfast in the morning, he offered to appoint me an honorary director of the project and implied that, between us, we could flimflam the Sultan out of his stock. I literally had to peel him off me to embark for the airport; in his final frenzy he made a grab for my wristwatch, figuring, I suppose, that it was better than nothing. The agony on his face, as I last saw it through the bus window, was almost Promethean, though perhaps it was only the brandy pecking at his liver.

In the waiting room at the field was a racial fricassee comparable to the Tower of Babel; Indians, Africans, Arabs, Malagasy, Seychellois, and half a dozen other nationalities milled about, costumed as if for a Shubert musical and behaving with much the same incoherence. The majority, it was evident, had no connection with the tour beyond a desire to catch a glimpse of the ruler, who arrived with suitable pomp in a Rolls-Royce flaunting his dynastic red flag. He was a benevolent, patriarchal gentleman of seventy-odd attired in Arab dress, with a white beard and horn-rimmed spectacles, and I felt a wave of resentment at Mr. Tigris for assuming that I would ever whipsaw such a kindly old codger. When his entourage, and various British dignitaries, aviation officials, and similar consequential guests were finally stowed aboard the *Seyyid Said bin Sultan,* a DC-3 christened for the occasion after Zanzibar's earliest sovereign, we numbered eighteen souls. The flight to Pemba was idyllic save for a continuous grinding noise, which turned out to be the voice of my seatmate, an Indian businessman attached to the chamber of commerce. While his statistics on the decline of clove production were stimulating enough, the warm pressure of his lips on my ear ultimately gave me goose flesh, and I sought out another chair. The passenger next to me there, a well-set-up Briton and keen as horseradish, had an oddly familiar look. Putting two and two together, I decided it was Sorsbie, the chap who had invited me on the trip and who, obviously out of shyness, had given no indication he was going along himself. Just as I was framing an oblique reference to a mutual acquaintance of ours up in Paris, however, he excused himself abruptly and departed. It was one of those curious coincidences that occur nowhere but in East Africa.

Except that the speeches were in Arabic and Swahili and the audience more exotic, the ensuing ceremony at Pemba, held in a marquee pitched beside the runway, could have served equally to consecrate a supermarket in Los Angeles. An assemblage of several hundred sheiks, African elders, and Khoja Ismailis, liegemen of the Aga Khan, applauded vociferously as one after another of their spokesmen rose to hail the new era of prosperity and universal brotherhood that would attend regular air service. The rest of Pemba's male population—Mohammedan custom bars the presence of women at important functions—stood or crouched in the blazing sun, wilting under the interminable rhetoric but doggedly awaiting the refreshments scheduled to follow. At last, when everyone had run out of bromides, the Sultan's speech of acknowledgment in three languages was read into the microphone by his aide-de-camp, taking three times as long as a speech of acknowledgment in one language, and the tension abated. To the strains of that perennial Islamic favorite, "Easter Parade," rendered by a military band, a platoon of waiters distributed highly appropriate sweetmeats of molten Turkish paste, and steaming coffee. The visitors were now worshipfully directed to resume their places in the aircraft, so that it could proceed onward to Nairobi. As we did, the four or five ladies in the contingent, who had been concealed behind a stockade during the exercises, rejoined us, among them the Sultana and her lady in waiting. The two promptly immured themselves in the washroom to change their costumes, and thereby created a horrid dilemma for crew and passengers alike. The pilot, afraid it would be lèse-majesté to bang on the door, had to delay the takeoff until they reappeared, and we were all nicely parboiled by the time the plane was aloft.

My previous contact with royalty had been limited to two Asiatic playboys, in the persons of the crown prince of Johore and the ex-emperor of Annam, Bao Dai, neither of them monarchs to overshadow Charlemagne, and when my turn came to meet Their Highnesses, I was inclined to hang back. However, I reflected that they could hardly bite my head off, since their bridgework, like mine, must be immobilized by Turkish paste, and, assuming the expression of servility one uses on credit managers, I sidled up to them. The audience began a bit chaotically, for just as I made my curtsy, the plane hit an air pocket and threatened to catapult me into the Sultana's lap. Nevertheless, by flailing around briskly, I caught hold of a gentlewoman's chignon across the aisle and recovered my balance. Kaleidoscopic though it was, my first impression of the Sultana was glamorous. A gazelle-eyed matron clad in a filmy blue sari, she wore a necklace of emblematic gold coins and matching bangles, and a square-cut emerald approximately the size of a Congress playing card.

"Well, this a red-letter day for yours truly, sir," I assured the Sultan, deciding to adopt a straightforward, democratic line. "Little did I think a month ago that I would be shooting the breeze with a real Arab potentate two thousand feet up in the air. Actually," I commented, with a smile, "it's kind of a switch, isn't it? Shouldn't we all be seated on a flying carpet?"

"What did the young man say?" inquired His Highness, regarding me in perplexity.

"Something about a carpet," his wife said uncertainly. "I think he's trying to sell us one."

"We don't need any," the Sultan replied, with unnecessary force. "The house is full of them. Tell him to go away."

Amused that they had mistaken me for a salesman, I went back to the very beginning in Paris and described how I chanced to be present, not omitting a friendly injunction to beware of Tigris and his dubious casino. To fix the details firmly in his mind, and at the same time demonstrate that I had his undivided attention, the Sultan closed his eyes. He was very much *au courant,* though, because the moment I concluded, they flew wide-open again.

"What happened? Who are you?" he demanded. "Why are you looking at my wife's ring like that?"

"I was only admiring it," I stammered. "I've never seen such a headlight before."

"We-ell, all right," he said suspiciously, "but don't get any crazy ideas, Jack."

The ease with which he had slipped into the vernacular startled me. "Your Highness is at home in the American idiom?" I queried.

"Oh, I dig it a little," he admitted, visibly flattered. "You may think we're squares down here, but we see *Variety* and

Down Beat and all those publications. One of my sultanic whims is to keep up with the box-office grosses and the different pop tunes. You know," he went on reflectively, "to me there's nothing worse than a suzerain who becomes insular. Of course, if he's an insular suzerain like I to begin with, that's different, but I believe that a man which he is the spiritual and political leader of a heterogeneous flock had ought to keep his finger on the pulse of the common man."

"It figures," I concurred. "If memory serves, the fabled Haroun-al-Rashid ofttimes used to dress up in rags and mingle with his subjects in the bazaar. Does Your Highness ever do that?"

"I don't have to dress up, the way things are going in Zanzibar," he observed gloomily. "Would you like some lugubrious statistics on the decline of clove production there?"

I would have loved it, but the plane was already over the outskirts of Nairobi, and whispers of a reception at the airdrome were circulating through the cabin. Within a few minutes, we were standing on terra firma, our heads bared to a salute from a guard of honor. The group photograph in next day's newspaper identified only the Sultan and a couple of his Ministers, charitably ignoring the man behind them struggling to detach a passport from a toupee. I got a letter from Sorsbie shortly afterward with a bill enclosed from Tigris for six brandies. He asked what the devil it meant and begged me not to explain. Curious race, the English. Once they warm up, there's no telling what they'll do for you.

Battle of Calabash

William Brandon

Linwood Yuitt and John Broom both came to Calabash in the same winter. Mr. Broom went to work for Mr. Hochsettler on the Republican, which was the Democratic paper. Mr. Yuitt came the following month and hung up his derby hat in the shop of the Democrat, which was the Republican paper, and went to work without a word to anybody. He had been there two days before Miss Fresian, who owned the Democrat, knew who he was; but then Miss Fresian was new to the newspaper business.

The first thing I remember hearing Mr. Yuitt say was, "Cheer up, the worst is yet to come," when Miss Fresian discovered that he was the new printer and told him that though he was paid by the thousand ems he was not—even when drinking—to spell waffle "wafflffle" as he had done in the story of the church supper. He was a very good typesetter and complaints didn't bother him. He never made excuses.

He was a tall thin man with a thick mustache and a baggy pocketful of leads. He had bright, blue, kindly eyes. And he had certain gentlemanly ways. He pared his tobacco with a knife and swallowed his spit in the presence of a lady.

He was young enough to take a shine to Miss Fresian. But John Broom, on the Republican, was younger still, and that's how the poetical war came about.

The job of working local poet was always bestowed on the current printer. That was the Age of the Itinerant Printer, who was traditionally a man of many parts. If he was a genuine inspirational poet he made up his verses out of his own head, setting them up in type as he went along. If he was a manufactured poet he used a pencil and paper, a bottle of whisky, and the newspaper's rhyming dictionary wherewith to change the last words of the lines he lifted from Pope or Dryden.

Linwood Yuitt and John Broom were both legitimate poets who composed their stuff directly out of the type case. If Mr. Yuitt and Mr. Broom could have had their way, the Calabash Republican and the Calabash Democrat would have been printed entirely in verse. That was what almost happened, before the great Calabash Battle of the Poets was over.

When Mr. Yuitt came to the Democrat, John Broom had already met Miss Fresian and had taken her to a Halloween social and was calling her Lucy. Mr. Yuitt's natural antagonism toward any opposition paper was outraged by this situation.

Miss Fresian was an old maid in her middle twenties but she was still very good-looking. My aunt usually referred to Miss Fresian as a shameless hoyden, but I thought she was pretty slick and high-toned. My aunt didn't think Miss

Fresian's newspaper was a good place for a young boy like me to be employed, but my uncle put his foot down and said it was never too early to start.

Around the shop Miss Fresian was lively. She cussed whenever she wanted to and whirled her petticoats in an engaging way when she hoisted herself upon a stack of type cases to sit a while and talk, and Mr. Yuitt at such times would confuse his fonts. . . .

Miss Fresian had a lot of independence, which she came by naturally. Only a few years before, her father, old Mr. Fresian, had singlehandedly taken on the Knights of the Flaming Cross. The Knights were an organization bent on cleaning up sin in Calabash. The first thing they set out to do was burn down the Red Hot Opera House, a place below the Nickel Plate tracks owned and operated by a lady known as Peppersauce Sal. Mr. Fresian himself went to the Red Hot Opera House and helped Peppersauce Sal cool off the Knights with boilers of hot water tossed from the roof, and after that Mr. Fresian lambasted the organization in the Democrat and tore it apart so thoroughly it never was put together again.

Peppersauce Sal went on with her high-rolling ways at the Red Hot Opera House and Miss Fresian made a point of being friendly to her, which my aunt said was a scandal. My uncle said it only showed Lucy was as bang-up independent as old Mr. Fresian had been, and that was a good thing for the town.

In the shop Mr. Yuitt didn't say much to Miss Fresian. I guessed he didn't think she was a good business manager, but he didn't say so. Miss Fresian let subscriptions run until the subscribers paid out of a sense of shame, and she went on selling advertising to storekeepers who were five years behind in payments. The paper was in debt; but the notes were held by Walter Howard Plinge, another of her father's friends, who had promised not to call them in for ten years.

I heard her explain to John Broom that her father had run the paper on nothing but friendliness and honesty and that she intended to do the same.

When Mr. Yuitt would take off his apron at the end of a day's work, he would square his derby on his head and walk into the office and lift his hat and say, "Good evening," to Miss Fresian. Then he would swallow a few times and say good evening again and lift his hat again, and leave. However, one afternoon he got up the courage to ask Miss Fresian if he might call on her after supper.

She told him she was going someplace with Mr. Broom, but perhaps the next night Mr. Yuitt would go with her to the minstrel show. Mr. Yuitt said he sure would, and ran into the wall on his way out.

When the Republican came out next, John Broom ran a poem in it about Mr. Yuitt. It was a good high-caliber poem, or rather song, set to the tune of Pick Up the Pawpaws and Put 'Em in a Basket. It described the adventures of Deadwood shopping for a casket, Deadwood being a play on Mr. Yuitt's first name of Linwood. There was a reference to the show Mr. Yuitt had taken Miss Fresian to see. The poem said that a minstrel had strung up Deadwood and played him for a banjo, twanged his mustache and thumped on his esophagus and showed him off for a musical cuss.

Miss Fresian told Mr. Yuitt she thought the song was wonderful and she hoped Mr. Yuitt would give it an answer. Mr. Yuitt smiled and told her to cheer up, the worst was yet to come.

That night Mr. Broom, all smiles, escorted Miss Fresian to the Christian Endeavor Penny Supper. The next night Mr. Yuitt took Miss Fresian to the Odd Fellows Ball.

In the next issue of the Democrat, Mr. Yuitt replied to John Broom with a metrical cannonading. Mr. Yuitt was not confined to mere printer doggerel. He could be a champion poet. His satire was built of majestic, imposing fifteeners balanced against one another with a nice equivalence, alternating one of lightning with one of thunder.

In Indiana, as everyone knows, all children who can learn to spell immediately take up the practice of literature. Those who can't spell go into politics. So the town received Mr. Yuitt's poem with awe and then a roar of pure delight.

Probably the two lines that hit John Broom the hardest dealt with the meager quality of his baby verse, fragile as a butterfly, and with Mr. Broom's secret habit of exercising with dumbbells, a fact Mr. Yuitt had unearthed by spying on Mr. Broom's boardinghouse. The poem complimented Mr. Broom on the graceful lines of his figure and his plump bust, that it said any barred Rock would be proud to own, but cautioned Mr. Broom about the danger of bursting himself with dumbbell well-being. It asked him to consider why pops the pod if not with health.

John Broom was an earnest and sensitive young man. He was rather small, barely taller than Miss Fresian, but he had a tough, roosterlike walk and manner that made him seem big. He had a serious mind and sometimes went to church. He was very saving. He intended to own his own newspaper someday. He never drank except for an occasional neat glass of whisky in the home of the Walter Howard Plinges, when he visited there with Miss Fresian. He dressed well, for a printer.

He came into the shop the day after the appearance of Mr. Yuitt's poem. He walked up to Mr. Yuitt and took his arm and turned him from his work. Miss Fresian snatched up a copy book and ran in from the office and said, "John Broom! Don't you dare start any trouble in here!"

John Broom gave her a bland look. He said, "Why, I want to shake this gentleman's hand."

Miss Fresian watched him with suspicion.

"That was a pretty good thing you wrote," John Broom said.

"Well, thanks," Mr. Yuitt said mildly.

They shook hands. Mr. Yuitt's manner was pleasant but in his left hand, out of sight, he held a stick of type like a club. John Broom continued to smile, but the look in his eyes showed what it cost him.

"You made a mite free with painting up a dactyl for an iambus," John Broom said, "but otherwise it ain't too bad at all."

"Maybe the next time I'll unlimber my bravura caesura," Mr. Yuitt said.

"You do that, friend," John Broom said. He dropped Mr. Yuitt's hand and walked into Miss Fresian's office, a smile frozen on his face. Miss Fresian followed him. I sidled over and hung around the Dutchman's gate between the shop and the office. John Broom had stopped smiling. He said, "I'm going to run that baboon out of town. He made me look like a girl."

"Oh, hush. And please run along; we're busy."

"Am I still invited to come and call on you this evening?"

"Of course you are," Miss Fresian said, impatient and indulgent. "Goodness! You started it, didn't you?"

"I'll bravura his caesura," John Broom said in a strangled voice. He went out and slammed the door.

In the Republican on the following Wednesday, John Broom showed Calabash that he too had been traveling under wraps. He tore into Mr. Yuitt in a full column of excellent blank verse. He savaged Mr. Yuitt a while and then laid him out and skinned him by the inch and dismembered him and left him hanging in a smokehouse of ridicule.

Calabash was overjoyed. The town read the poem with the exquisite pleasure of cannibals watching the slow roasting of a fat, tender captive.

Somehow John Broom had learned that Mr. Yuitt kept a hair ribbon of Miss Fresian's in an old tobacco box and slept with it under his pillow at night. The verses drew a portrait of a pathetic old man, his hair low cut in bangs across his brow, his mouth agape, his mustache all over his face, pawing a ribbon stolen from a lovely young maiden who was revolted by the very sight and smell of him and shuddered under his ivory eyes, which turned up like fishes' bellies afloat in yellow whisky.

Mr. Yuitt stayed away from work for half the next day. When he came to the shop he had had his hair cut and he smelled of cologne. He had nothing to say to anyone. He went through his work with a grim preoccupation. He was feeling low—that was obvious. Miss Fresian sat at her desk humming a tune and paid no attention to him at all.

At the end of the day Mr. Yuitt stalked in to her and said abruptly, "Lucy, are you revolted by the sight of me?"

Miss Fresian said, "Linwood, don't be so silly."

"Say the word and I'll get my hat and go on my way," Mr. Yuitt said.

"You won't do any such thing," Miss Fresian said. "That's what he wants you to do." They looked at each other for a time, then Miss Fresian said, "You're my printer and I need a printer. If you and John can't write these poems without losing your heads, then stop writing them."

"I don't like the way he dragged you into it!" Mr. Yuitt said.

"He didn't say anything to injure me, did he?"

"I ain't any old man!" Mr. Yuitt shouted. "I ain't even forty! If I'd shave I'd look younger'n he does! *He* can't even grow a mustache!"

Miss Fresian began to laugh, and he said, "Listen, do I smell?"

"Just of printer's ink and whisky and tobacco."

"Well, is it revolting?" Mr. Yuitt demanded.

"It's what I was born to," Miss Fresian said.

Mr. Yuitt tugged at his mustache. He said in a voice like a croak, "Are you still going to the musical with me tonight?"

Miss Fresian made her eyes wide and said, "Why on earth shouldn't I?"

Mr. Yuitt's poem in Friday's Democrat was an ode to a corset on a broom. Now whether John Broom really wore a corset or not was never settled; but his clothes were up to the last mark of the pinch-waisted style and he could have worn a corset. Emotionally, Calabash was convinced by Mr. Yuitt's merciless couplets that John Broom did wear a corset, and that he clung to the bedpost while his trained dumbbells drew the strings and hooked it up for him.

Calabash expected something special now in each round of this poetical war, and the town was never disappointed. When it would seem that one or another of the contestants must have outdone himself, the poet next week would produce a broadside still more exalted, more cruel, more lyric or heroic as the case demanded.

It was a battle of the giants, the gods rolling mountains upon each other, and it was no wonder that the harvesting was a little later that year.

The two bards were fairly evenly matched, but there was a basic difference in their styles. John Broom liked blank verse and he stayed closer to earth in his allusions. He liked to talk in hard country language. Mr. Yuitt was more of the high-flown school. He favored the heroic couplet and he usually introduced himself with a prayer to Demeter, or a line beginning "O that my Muse," and so forth, or, "When to the skies I reach to pluck my lyre." Mr. Yuitt also elided vowels freely.

The town didn't divide on partisan lines. There were too many angles. Red-hot Democrats would be more likely to favor John Broom, as the voice of the Democratic paper; but the Democrats had a natural fondness for Mr. Yuitt, while aristocratic Republicans, as typified by the Walter Howard Plinges, whose outhouse was built in the style of a lavish

Oriental pagoda, were attracted by John Broom's fine man-
ners and imposing presence. John Broom's most ardent sup-
porter, in fact, was Mrs. Walter Howard Plinge.

But old folks were alienated from the Broom camp by repeated attacks on Mr. Yuitt's alleged old age, and the town
dandies were displeased by Mr. Yuitt's scorn of John
Broom's up-to-date dress and accessories.

Others sided with John Broom because his poems usually
ran longer than Mr. Yuitt's. But Yuitt enthusiasts claimed
that John Broom heaped up his words for effect, such as
talking about them "sturdy strapping galluses, them long-
bowed snapping galluses, that Ma used for the greaser in the
pan," and, "Towser et them snapping galluses, them sturdy
long-bowed galluses," and so on—something about they
stretched and came up looking like a man, presumably Mr.
Yuitt. Mr. Yuitt, they said, didn't need to pile his lines together to hide the fact that they weren't well made, or that
his images were weak. He hung the hide of his opponent on
the barn door of heaven and nailed it there with stars in
lines that were as clean-cut as so many Green River knives.

A decision couldn't be forced either way; something had to
give sooner or later, and Mr. Hochsettler came up with the
answer. It was arranged that at the harvest festivities in Foster Park the two poets would each read a poem. A committee headed by Mr. Homer Tucker, a full-time professional
poet from Indianapolis, would judge between them. The
winner would be given a suitable trophy. The rivals would
shake hands in the presence of the entire town. And the war
would be over.

My sentiments were all for Mr. Yuitt. I was confident of
his victory. But on the evening before the battle I overheard
his ruin.

It had been a busy day, but Mr. Yuitt was grinning to himself and was in a wonderful humor. Whenever the office was

clear of people he would go in and say to Miss Fresian, "Listen here," again, and Miss Fresian would say, "Yes?" again, but he was never able to get any further.

At the end of the day he made a great effort and said, "Listen here," in a voice like a shout; and when Miss Fresian said, "Yes?" he struggled manfully with his tongue and blurted at last, "Maybe we better talk about it tomorrow." Miss Fresian asked what they would talk about tomorrow. Mr. Yuitt tugged his mustache, swallowed several times, and said, "Cheer up, the worst is yet to come." He charged out of the office and went loping away down the street.

When I came back after supper to sweep out the shop Miss Fresian was still in the office, and John Broom was talking to her. They looked as if they had been talking a long time. They were very solemn.

I sat down in the shop just beyond the office door and listened.

"Then forget all that and just give me your straight answer on a straight proposition," John Broom said.

"I can't give you an answer," Miss Fresian said. "I can't think what to do. I promised Papa, that's all."

"You can't live on a promise," John Broom said. "You don't know how to handle a small town like this, that's your big trouble. Anyhow, it takes a mighty smart man to make any paper give him a living these days."

"I've been making a go of it," Miss Fresian said.

"No use kidding yourself," John Broom said. "Like I say, you don't know how to make the community support you. You can't be contrary and independent in a small town. You've got to be as slick as a politician, and agree with everybody. I can take this paper and I can own this town before I'm through. Lucy, I told you I've been saving my money because I want to settle down and amount to something. This is the chance I've always been looking for. You can't expect me not to grab it, can you? Be sensible and say yes."

Miss Fresian began to cry. She said, "There doesn't seem to be anything else I can say now."

I lined out the back door of the shop and went looking for Mr. Yuitt. Somebody told me he was in the Main Street Saloon but when I tried to go in there after him, the bartender, Mr. Gulahy, a Broom man, threw me out.

Then I saw Peppersauce Sal on the street, carrying a pink parasol. She was very beautiful. I supposed hell would swallow me up if I ever spoke to Peppersauce Sal but I went up and spoke to her anyway.

I told her that Miss Fresian had said yes to Mr. Broom. She said Mr. Broom was a little piccolo. I said it wouldn't matter if Mr. Yuitt won the battle or not now, because he would probably go out and cut his throat when he heard about Miss Fresian and Mr. Broom. I said that anyway Mr. Yuitt would be fired from his job because Mr. Broom was going to own the Democrat. Peppersauce Sal said we'd all be damned and that Mr. Yuitt would keep in there in the saloon, and that she'd better have a talk first with Miss Fresian. She snapped up her parasol, although it was dark by then, and sailed away.

All of Calabash turned out in Foster Park the next day. Mr. Broom was up on the speaker's platform with Mr. Hochsettler. Homer Tucker sat to one side with the literary committee, all ladies except for Mr. Tucker.

I couldn't find Mr. Yuitt or Miss Fresian but a few minutes before the poetical contest was to get started I saw Peppersauce Sal again. I spoke to her, although the whole town was there to see.

She shook her finger at me and said, "Everything's just fine." I said what about Miss Fresian saying yes. "That little piccolo was trying to buy out the paper," Peppersauce Sal said. "Lucy didn't want to let it go because she promised her papa she'd keep it in the family, but he'd bought up those notes Mr. Plinge held. Mrs. Plinge made that spineless husband of hers sell them because she said he hadn't promised not to sell them, even though he had promised not to call them for ten years, and Mrs. Plinge thinks that little piccolo told Lucy she could either sell out to him right now or meet the notes on the first of the month."

I said Mr. Broom would get the paper anyway, because Miss Fresian didn't have any money. "Just let Mr. Yuitt handle that," Peppersauce Sal said. "She didn't have the face to tell him about it, but I sure did."

I pointed out that Mr. Yuitt, being a more typical printer than Mr. Broom, didn't have a red cent.

"He's got something worth a sight more," Peppersauce Sal said. "He's got gumption. Just see that you yell your head off at the right time. I've got all the musicians and the ladies of the ensemble from the opera house scattered around to lead the yelling too. All we need is to get 'em started." She told me not to worry, everything would be just fine, and then my aunt grabbed me and dragged me away.

A great shout went up from the crowd, and when my aunt turned me loose I climbed a tree and saw Mr. Yuitt on the platform. He took off his derby hat and waved it.

When there was silence Mr. Yuitt said, "I've throwed away the poem I aimed to read to you. Instead of it I've got a bigger poem than a piece of paper will hold. It's a poem you folks will have to help write."

There were a few questioning cheers.

"A man started a newspaper in Calabash County because he liked it here," Mr. Yuitt said. "He could have settled anywheres else in the world but he concluded that Calabash County was the best danged spot in the universe."

The ladies of the ensemble shrieked and Mr. Yuitt was silenced again by the enthusiastic roar of the crowd.

"When he passed beyond," Mr. Yuitt went on, "he asked his daughter Lucy to keep on agoing the way he'd been headed. He never had a mean thought and he never spoke a dishonest word, and the only tune he ever played was the one he believed was right, regardless of who might not like the music. His daughter Lucy has tried to follow that same road."

Folks began yelling for Miss Fresian, but she didn't appear.

"That's the way she's tried to handle things too. But now she has been given an offer to either sell her newspaper or get put out of business."

There was a low growl from the crowd, like a sudden roll of thunder.

"The party that made this offer said this town.was against her," Mr. Yuitt said. The thunder became a lightning clap. "She wants to keep her life here in Calabash County where it belongs. But if Calabash County don't want her running the Democrat, why, that's a different story. So she'd like to hear from you folks right now."

The crowd bellowed and the band played, before the ladies of the ensemble could even lead them off. Mr. Yuitt got them quiet again.

He said, "The way she wants to hear is with hard cash. If she's going to keep the Democrat she needs cash and plenty of it. You folks that owe back bills, and any of you folks that want to pay for subscriptions and advertising in advance, it's up to you."

Before the exuberant voice of the crowd could drown him out again, he said, "Now you're wondering where I've got a right to get up here and talk this way about a poem that by rights ain't mine. Well, we're coming to the part that really sounds like poetry to me. Miss Lucy Fresian has just now become Mrs. Linwood Yuitt at a quiet ceremony performed at noon in the parsonage of the Methodist Episcopal Church."

The crowd yelled so loud it stripped leaves off the trees.

"The happy couple," Mr. Yuitt continued, "will leave on the three-fifteen from the Nickel Plate depot for a short wedding trip. But right now the proprietor of the Calabash Democrat is waiting in her office to see whether or not you folks want her to keep that job. Until three o'clock she will accept payments in cash or goods for bills past due or for subscriptions or advertising space in advance. There's the poem, you folks finish it."

He waved his derby hat and jumped off the platform and tried to make his way through the park. The crowd took him up on its shoulders and marched behind the band to the Democrat office.

It was said that John Broom recited a fine poem, his very best, worthy of the silver-plated shaving mug Mr. Tucker presented to him as the prize. But not many heard it, most of the town being over at the Democrat office paying bills, and later marching Mr. Yuitt and Miss Fresian over to the depot to catch the train.

Miss Fresian said a few words from the step of their car, about how proud it made her to belong to them, and then the crowd wouldn't let Mr. Yuitt go without one last poem. He said he'd give them one.

He stood up and said, "Cheer up, the worst is yet to come."

Sorry, Right Number!

Jean C. Clark

From where she sat at the reception desk, Maryann Mason could look out through the rain-streaked window, lettered "Ann's Beauty Shop," into the downpour in the street. It had seemed a stroke of genius six months ago, when she had opened her place, to call it *Ann's* Beauty Shop. It meant that her name would head the list of beauty shops in the new directories. But now she was resigned to the fact that it was going to take much more than a stroke of genius to make her a success.

The telephone rang, but even before she lifted it, Maryann knew it would not be for her. "Good morning," she said softly. "Ann's Beauty Shop."

"Ain't this Joe's Television Shop?" an unpleasant male voice rasped.

"No. I'm afraid you dialed the wrong number."

"Well, what's the right number?"

She told him, and there was a loud click in her ear. It was like Joe's customers not to say thank you.

Well, the morning was off to its usual start. Three calls for Joe's Television Shop. None for her. There were times when Maryann wished that she were the kind of person who could walk over to Joe's and give the fellow, whoever he was, a piece of her mind. The phone rang again. And this time it turned out to be Mrs. Gilfregus, Maryann's only regular customer so far.

"Your line's been *busy!*" Mrs. Gilfregus said.

"More of those wrong numbers—for Joe's Television Shop."

"Well, if I were you, Ann, I'd go over and see that Joe. Ask him to have his number changed."

"Oh, I couldn't. I wouldn't dare."

"Nonsense. Flutter your eyelashes at him. You can catch more flies with honey, I always say." And then she canceled her appointment because of the rain.

After she hung up, Maryann sat and brooded for a while. If she went to see this Joe, he'd probably throw her out. "If only I were a big blonde," Maryann thought. "Forceful and aggressive. Not afraid of anybody. Then people wouldn't push me around."

Glancing in the mirror, she could see why people took advantage of her, why she was always the last one waited on in stores. With her brown eyes and diffident smile, she looked like a person who practically made a career of holding doors open for people. Just plain meek. But why, she wondered, did people also take advantage of her over the phone? Was her voice that soft and hesitant?

The telephone rang again. "I'm a big bosomy bleached blonde," Maryann told herself before she answered it. "I'm forceful and aggressive and I'm not afraid of anybody." She bellowed into the phone, "Ann's Beauty Shop."

"Oh, I'm awfully sorry," said an apologetic voice. "I was calling Joe's Television. Excuse me for bothering you."

Maryann's eyes grew round. It worked! So why shouldn't she call this Joe and tell him about the trouble he was causing her? Right now—while she was in the mood? Taking a deep breath, she dialed Joe's number.

"Joe's Television Shop," said a deep pleasant male voice.

"This is Ann's Beauty Shop." Her voice was delightfully imperious. "My line is constantly tied up with your calls. I've decided it would be a good idea if you had your number changed."

"Hey!" he said. "If you're bothered so much, why not change yours?"

"Mine is not the faulty number. Yours ends in a zero, and people don't dial it all the way."

"You're crazy."

"I am not. For two cents I'd come over to your place and give you a piece of my mind."

"You come right ahead, lady," he said. "I'm not afraid of you."

Maryann hung up, shaking all over. She couldn't go over to Joe's, of course. It was one thing to talk that way over the telephone—another to face a stranger and tell him off.

The telephone rang. Maryann picked it up, and before she could speak, a voice said, "Hey, my aerial just fell down!"

"This," Maryann said firmly, "is *not* Joe's Television Shop."

The call was just what she needed to fortify her crumbling resolve. She put on her raincoat and sloshed the two blocks down the street and around the corner to Joe's.

She went in and immediately felt limp with fright. "I'm a big blonde," she whispered to herself, but her heart kept pounding frantically.

And then a lanky young man, with light hair that needed cutting, came out from the workshop at the back. "Oh, boy," he said, "am I glad to see *you!*"

Maryann's heart swooped heavily. This was the same voice she'd heard over the phone. But she hadn't dreamed he'd be so young—so likable-looking, so friendly. Her voice was little more than a whisper. "Why should you be glad to see *me?*"

"Well, I'll tell you. Any minute now that door will open, and in will burst a big buxom bleached blonde. She's planning to give me a piece of her so-called mind. But with you here, she won't dare say much."

"You're not *afraid* of her, are you?"

"Sure I am." He smiled, and Maryann's heart took another plunge. "If you stick around till she's gone, I'll buy your dinner tonight. How's that for a fair exchange?"

"Well, I don't know. I mean, I—are you sure this woman is a big blonde?"

"Positive. You may not believe it, but she wants me to change my telephone number. After I've spent months building up my name and number and my slogan: 'No pix? Joe fix.' "

"Well, *uh* . . . now, look, Joe—maybe this woman has a good reason . . ."

"You," said Joe, "are obviously so sweet and feminine that you couldn't imagine a woman like this one." He hesitated and then stepped a little closer. "Tell me, are you interested in a TV set?"

Why, Maryann asked herself, did this man have to be Joe? She had come prepared to dislike him, but now . . . She sighed deeply and looked up at him. "Awfully interested," she heard herself say.

A big bosomy brunette looked belligerently in the show window, and Joe paled. "There she is," he whispered. "Don't leave me."

The big brunette looked Maryann up and down; she

looked Joe up and down; she looked around at the merchandise. Then she slowly moved on.

"What did I tell you?" Joe demanded. "I knew she'd lose her nerve when she saw I wasn't unprotected. I could have sworn, though, that she'd be a blonde. Now, about that dinner . . ."

"Forget it," Maryann said quickly. "Besides, I have a confession to make. I didn't come here to look at TV sets."

He smiled. "I know. I understand."

"You do?" Her breath almost stopped.

"Sure. You came in to get out of the rain. Lots of folks do that."

Maryann glanced toward the street. It was still raining. Why did she have the feeling the sun had come out? "I'd better be going," she said.

"Wait. I promised you dinner. What's your name and where do you live?"

"Maryann Mason. And I live at 23 East Main. But honestly—"

"I'll see you at seven," he said. His fingers rested lightly on her shoulder, and for the first time in six months she didn't feel lonely or pushed around or meek.

All that evening Maryann kept waiting for just the right moment to tell Joe she was Ann as well as Maryann. But the chance just didn't come up.

He took her to the Gold Room, where there was a small orchestra. "We have a lot of getting acquainted to do," he said during dinner. "Do you work—or is that a silly question?"

"That's a silly question. Of course I work."

"What do you do? No, don't tell me. You're a secretary. I can just see you typing beautiful letters, being kind to unwelcome callers, being sweet to people over the phone." His face darkened. "Not like that Ann at the beauty shop."

This was the moment. "Joe, I—"

"Just the type I can't stand. I like feminine women—your type." He gave her a sideways grin. "Do you by any chance like my type?"

The way he was looking at her made her breathless. "Tell me about your type," she said hesitantly.

And he did. He'd always been interested in fixing things. The folks back home had said he could fix anything but a broken heart. He went on talking, and they danced and talked, and Maryann felt she had never had such a good time in her whole life.

"We clicked," she thought after he had left her at her door. And tomorrow, she decided, she would tell him who she was. They could laugh about it. Maybe someday it would become a family joke.

She awakened full of steely resolves, and at noon, after a morning bright with sun and new customers, she closed her shop and walked to Joe's.

Her heart gave a jump when she saw how his face brightened at the sight of her.

"Ha!" he said. "You just can't keep away from me, can you?" He clasped both her hands. "Fact is, I'd be over at your place, begging you to have lunch, only I didn't give you a chance to tell me where you work."

"Joe," she said, "how about coming out for a little walk with me. I have something to tell you."

"Nothing bad, I hope. You're not a murderer out on bail? You aren't married? You haven't five kids?"

"No, Joe." She was laughing then.

They walked around the corner and down the street, and Maryann stopped under her sign. "Joe—" she said. And then over her shoulder she saw Mrs. Gilfregus bearing down on them.

"Well," said Mrs. Gilfregus. "I see you two are settling

your differences. I told you, Ann, you'd catch more flies with honey." She turned to Joe. "I knew that once you'd met Ann, you'd be only too glad to change your phone number."

"Ann?" he said. He glanced up at the sign. "Ann . . . Maryann."

"Joe," said Maryann, "I—"

"This business of catching flies with honey is a great system," he said to Mrs. Gilfregus. "And Maryann—Ann—is especially good at it. I prefer the direct approach myself."

"Ann's a great little career girl," Mrs. Gilfregus said. "Her beauty shop means everything to her."

"I'm sure it does," Joe said stiffly. "And I just remembered an urgent service call I have to make." He nodded abruptly and walked away.

"An odd duck," Mrs. Gilfregus said.

"I thought he was sweet," Maryann said, her voice trembling.

"Don't tell me he got *you* to change your telephone number?"

"No. But I would have. I'd even have changed my name." Her shoulders drooped. "Good-by, Mrs. Gilfregus. Give me a ring when you want a finger wave."

Maryann went up the stairs to her shop.

She spent the afternoon contemplating her bleak future, her many faults, and her broken heart. She shouldn't have tried to be a big blonde. She wasn't the type. She should never have gone into business for herself. She should have been a secretary. She could even have been Joe's secretary. If things had started differently, they could have been married. Until there were children, she could work in the store with Joe. She could type his orders and bills. And she could answer the telephone. "Joe's Television Shop," she could say.

At her elbow the phone rang. She picked it up. "Joe's Television Shop," she said in a dreamy voice.

A man's voice said, "I can't get anything on my TV but a little bright light in the center of the screen. Can Joe fix it right away?"

"He's out on an urgent service call," Maryann said. "I'm sorry."

"Well, get ahold of him, will you?" the man went on. "I want the set fixed by tonight." He gave her his name and address.

She hung up and looked dreamily at the phone. Then her eyes cleared. "Oh, my goodness!" she said aloud. "I really took down a real message. Whatever made me do it? Now I'll have to take it over to Joe."

There was a hollow feeling inside her as she walked down the street. What if he refused to speak to her? But he couldn't refuse. This was business.

A man passed her, mumbling to himself, and she turned. "Joe!"

He stopped. "Maryann!" He appeared embarrassed. "I was going to visit you. I have a message for you."

"Oh, Joe!" She felt guiltier than ever. "You mean you've been getting calls for me?"

He grinned. "Well, yes. But I never minded too much. And today I was glad. I want to apologize, Maryann. I realize you tried to tell me who you were any number of times. Oh, here's your message."

Maryann took the paper and read:

"Mrs. Gil Fregus wants her finger waved tomorrow."

She managed to keep her face serious. "Thank you, Joe." And then, "Oh, I have a message for you, too." She felt her cheeks flush. "I guess I left it on my desk. Anyway, some man says there's only a little bright light in the center of his screen. Can you fix it?"

"Maryann." His gaze was warm. "I can fix anything but a broken heart."

Suddenly it was just as it had been the day before and the evening before and the first thing at noon. In fact, it was even better. Maryann sighed happily and smiled up at him.

He took her hand, and they started up the street together.

"On second thought," he said. "I believe I can fix broken hearts, too."

Nuts in the Fruitcake

James Trager

Americans are so concerned with their health that our foods are advertised at least as much for their nutritional values as for their qualities of taste and pleasure. Much of our nutrition consciousness has developed in the past quarter-century.

People who never knew a calorie from a vitamin, if indeed they had ever heard those words, learned in the mess halls of World War II—or from young men returned from military service—that there is more to good eating than corn pone, fried pork and hot biscuits.

Millions of Americans in the 1940's shifted from fats and carbohydrates to foods with higher protein content. More grown men drank milk and orange juice and ate leafy green vegetables, even if they did not go on eating creamed chipped beef (made from cured, smoked, dehydrated chip-sliced beef round) on toast, a dish well remembered by servicemen for its earthy nickname.

This awareness of good nutrition has been a useful thing for the country. But America's interest in the health aspects of food has had its less fortunate side.

The country has often been swept by the campaigns of food faddists. We have no monopoly on such faddists. In their own ways, Confucius, Lao-Tze, Zoroaster, Siddhartha Gautama (The Buddha) and Moses all promulgated views about food and nutrition.

VEGETARIANS PAST AND PRESENT

One of the earliest and most persistent food mystiques has been vegetarianism, which can be based on the sort of sensibilities that prevent Hindus from killing any living thing or from attitudes about health.

Hindus are vegetarians, many of them because they believe it is healthier to live on a vegetarian diet. Trappist monks are vegetarians, too, and so are various occult groups and small Protestant sects like the Seventh Day Adventists, some of whose members operate Worthington Foods, a U.S. corporation active in producing meat-substitute analogs.

The poet Percy Bysshe Shelley published a treatise in 1813 which claimed the human digestive system was suited only to plant foods. . . .Shelley's thesis was taken quite seriously by George Bernard Shaw, who gave up eating meat when he was twenty-five. Some of Shaw's statements suggest, however, that he was more motivated by conscience than by science. "A man of my spiritual intensity," said GBS, "does not eat corpses."

Shaw maintained a vegetarian diet for the remainder of his ninety-four years* and claimed he was "seldom less than ten times as well as an ordinary carcass eater."

* "I don't like to peach on a pal," said H. G. Wells to Alexander Woollcott, "but Shaw cheats. He takes liver extract and calls it 'those chemicals.' " Mrs.

Another long-lived vegetarian, eighty-two when he died in 1910, was Leo Tolstoy. The Russian novelist and social critic proclaimed a new religion when he was forty-eight; it rejected sexuality, war, violence, drinking, smoking and the eating of animal flesh.

A few years earlier, in 1872, Samuel Butler in England had published a satirical novel, *Erewhon*, which kidded the vegetarians. Butler's fictional Erewhonians became vegetarians for reasons of moral scruple; one of them wrote a thesis on "The Rights of Vegetables." He went to some lengths to prove that vegetables, like animals, are alive and have feelings. Driven by logic to eat only such things as cabbages certified to have died of natural causes, the Erewhonians in the end gave up vegetarianism altogether.

. . . .

At the other extreme of the question are food extremists, like Gayelord Hauser whom we will discuss presently, who maintain that we should eat "living" foods and not "dead" ones.

Some vegetarians insist on eating raw vegetables, not cooked ones. Some call themselves "fruitarians" and eat only fruit. More permissive are the "lacto-vegetarians" who include milk, eggs and cheese in their diets, but other vegetarians say these are forms of meat and will not touch them.

One vegetarian argument has been that meat produces "necrones" and harmful deposits of uric acid in the body. An increase of uric acid in the blood is associated with diseases like gout; the body itself produces more uric acid when these diseases are present. But uric acid in the diet is not a *cause* of such diseases. As for necrones, no reputable doctor can tell you what they are.

Sensitivities aside, there are no convincing nutritional jus-

Patrick Campbell, in a stormy rehearsal of *Pygmalion*, cried out, "Shaw, some day you'll eat a pork chop and then God help all the women." But the day never came.

tifications for vegetarianism. Some vegetarians have, it is true, lived to ripe ages, but so have many meat eaters; more than one food fad, in fact, has recommended eating great quantities of meat. A 1948 book by Daniel C. Munro, *You Can Live Longer Than You Think,* claimed that Methuselah lived 969 years because he ate mostly meat. And then there was Dr. Salisbury of Salisbury steak fame.

No real correlation has ever been established between either a meat diet or a vegetarian diet and long life. Much of the world is forced by economic circumstance or religious law to subsist almost entirely without the primary sources of high-quality protein. Some amino acids and vitamin B_{12} are particularly hard to come by without animal protein.

But food fads and diet dogma tend to be simplistic and only dimly related to facts or realistic interpretations of facts. Some cultists have taken the fact that various bodily ills are accompanied by loss of appetite as evidence that long fasting has therapeutic value ("the body is trying to tell us something"). Upton Sinclair, whose novel *The Jungle* helped bring about the Pure Food and Drug Law, fell for this fasting nonsense. (He also defended vegetarianism, which his meat-packing exposés encouraged, and a number of other fads.) *The Fasting Cure,* which Sinclair wrote in 1911, claimed that prolonged fasting would be effective against tuberculosis, syphilis, asthma, cancer, the common cold, Bright's disease and liver trouble.

GRAHAM, THE CRACKER-BARREL EVANGELIST

One of America's first home-grown food faddists, and this country has had more than its share, was the Reverent Sylvester W. Graham, whose name survives in Graham flour and the Graham cracker.

Graham, a former Presbyterian preacher, was a temperance lecturer, vegetarian, dietetic "expert" and self-styled doctor of medicine. Born in West Suffield, Connecticut, in 1794, he launched an attack in his mid-thirties on meats and fats (which, he said, heated people's tempers and led them to sexual excesses). Condiments like mustard, catsup and pepper, he charged, could cause insanity.

Mostly he propagandized for a regimen of eating based on bread made from coarse, unbolted or unsifted flour and eaten slightly stale. The important thing was to keep the bran in the bread. Graham declared war on white bread, which had long been a symbol of good living and of Western civilization. He had no knowledge of the vitamins and minerals in bran, but like so many of his successors he was obsessed with bowel regularity; bran has laxative effects.

Graham neglected the fact that refined flour keeps better than whole grain flour in storage, and that it is easier to digest (bran irritates many people's intestines).

Indigestion, even the severe extremes of it called dyspepsia, were so common in early nineteenth-century America (Adams, Cooper and Volney all remarked about it) that Graham's teachings fell on fertile ground. Graham hotels sprang up around the country; and Graham followers, indoctrinated with ideas about eating more fruits and vegetables and less salt, shellfish and pork (Graham opposed them violently and barely tolerated milk, eggs and honey), included the founders of Oberlin College, John J. Shipherd and Philo Penfield Stewart; they included also Bronson Alcott (father of Louisa May who wrote *Little Women*), Joseph Smith, who founded the Mormon Church, Amelia Bloomer, the fashion revolutionary, and, from time to time, the inventor Thomas Edison and the journalist-editor-politician Horace Greeley.

Graham's philosophies of nutrition led, by way of the Adventist Church (whose spiritual leader, Mother Ellen Harmon White, promised God-given health and happiness to all who eschewed tobacco, salt, spices and spirits, drank only water and ate two meatless meals a day) to the whole modern breakfast food industry.

Mother White founded the Western Health Reform Institute at Battle Creek, Michigan, in 1866. Some years later, Dr. John Harvey Kellogg was hired to manage the Institute, whose name he changed to the Battle Creek Sanitarium, or the San, as it was called.

Patients at the San ate lots of bran in the Graham tradition. If they had high blood pressure, they were fed nothing but grapes—up to fourteen pounds of grapes a day. If thin, they were fed twenty-six times a day and forced to remain motionless lest they waste calories: they were not even allowed to brush their teeth.

Dr. Kellogg, with his brother Will K., developed a dry cereal called Granose; it sold 100,000 pounds its first year and went on from there.* A patient at the San, C. W. Post (whose nine months' stay did him no good), went on to invent Postum and Grape-Nuts.

Sylvester Graham, while he helped in a positive way to make America aware of the health aspects of food, unfortunately prepared the way for ensuing waves of food faddism and quackery.

---

*Today the breakfast food business is a $670 million industry and is highly competitive. There are some sixty-five nationally advertised brands (Kellogg has over forty per cent of the business), about twenty-five per cent of them less than eight years old. Health claims have always been effective in promoting cereal brands; one health claim in the future may involve dental health—some experimental work is being done to find cereal additives that will reduce tooth decay. For years, advertising was pitched strongly to children ("they're going to be with us longer," said the head of Kellogg) even though half the breakfast cereal output is eaten by adults. Lately, with the U.S. birth rate lower, the emphasis has been swinging to the geriatric market. Biggest seller is still Kellogg's Corn Flakes, with about ten per cent of the market.

Dietary apostles have appeared on the American scene regularly ever since. No doubt some of them have made valid contributions, if only by spurring scientists to find solid refutations to their claims. Many have also piled up sizable fortunes.

"CHEW EVERY BITE"

Britain's nineteenth-century Prime Minister William Gladstone, near the end of his career, said rather self-righteously, "I have made it a rule to give every tooth of mine a chance, and when I eat, to chew every bite thirty-two times. To this rule I owe much of my success in life."

An American businessman, Horace Fletcher, digested this pap and developed it into a system he called "Fletcherism." His book, *The ABC of Nutrition,* went into six editions between 1903 and 1905. "Nature will castigate those who don't masticate," was one of its precepts. Only five foot six, Fletcher weighed 217 pounds at age forty when he read Gladstone's statement. He went on a strict diet, chewed vigorously* and lost sixty-five pounds. He also overcame shortness of breath, but it was what he ate rather than how he ate it that made the difference.

Nevertheless, Fletcherism was a huge fad by the time Horace Fletcher died in 1919. It was taken up by Thomas Edison, John D. Rockefeller, the cadets at West Point, scientists at Harvard, Yale, Johns Hopkins, Cambridge University and the Sorbonne—and, of course, by Upton Sinclair, who met Fletcher at the Battle Creek Sanitarium.

The philosopher William James was a Fletcherite for three months. "I had to give it up," he said later. "It nearly killed me."

---

*Chewing is useful (it stimulates the digestive juices), but Fletcher and Gladstone went off the deep end.

Many food fads have been based on the idea that some foods should not be eaten together. If you avoid mixing pickles and milk, or fruit and milk or milk and potatoes, it may be a hangover of a food fad that influenced your mother or grandmother and was handed down in the family.

Did someone warn you in childhood that the acid in the fruit or the pickle would curdle the milk? What about the acid the milk will encounter in the stomach?

HAYISM AND OTHER MYTHS

The milk-and-potatoes injunction goes back to Dr. William Howard Hay whose 1933 book, *Health Via Food,* alleged that almost all bodily ills came from "acidosis." This, he said, was caused by eating too much protein, too much adulterated food like white bread, retention of food in the bowels more than twenty-four hours after eating and the combining of protein and carbohydrate.

Proteins, said Hay very solemnly, need acid for their digesting and carbohydrates require alkaline; "no human stomach can be expected to be acid and alkaline at the same time."

The fact is, most foods contain mixtures of proteins and starches. Facts, however, have never stood in the way of fads. Such, to echo Fabre, is human folly.

Hay also preached the gospel of frequent fasting, though fasting really *does* cause acidity, or "acidosis" as Hay called it.

Some widely believed food myths are less easily traced, but there are so many of them that almost everybody believes at least some of them. *None* of the following is true:

"Feed a cold, starve a fever."
Sweets cause adolescent acne.
Sugar in the diet causes diabetes.

Grapefruit, cottage cheese, yogurt, lemon juice and protein bread have positive powers to take off weight.

Sour cream is less fattening than sweet cream.

Honey is less fattening than sugar.

Diets high in red meats cause high blood pressure and kidney disease.

Avoid salt when trying to lose weight.

Ice cream or milk should not be taken at the same meal as shellfish.

Butter is rich in protein.

Bread and potatoes are fattening.

Brown eggs are more nutritious than white eggs.

White eggs are more nutritious than brown eggs.

Gelatin desserts are low in calories.

Beets make the blood thin.

Citrus fruits and tomatoes make the blood acid.

Eating big meals late in the day puts on more weight than eating heavily earlier in the day.

Veal is less nutritious than mature beef.

Toasting bread reduces its calorie content.

Hard-cooked eggs are hard to digest.

Thunderstorms curdle milk.

Applesauce served with greasy food absorbs excess grease.

Searing meat seals in the juices.

Basting meat with its own juices keeps it from drying out.

Black coffee is "stronger" than coffee with milk or cream.

Fish is brain food.

An apple a day keeps the doctor away.

We repeat: *none* of the above statements is true, no matter what you were brought up to believe.

While some people religiously avoid meat during the Lenten period, or religiously avoid serving meat and dairy products at the same meal, many more "religiously" follow unfounded beliefs like the ones we have listed.

LOOK DEEPER, LIVE SMARTER

Perhaps the most prominent diet and health mythologist in recent years has been Gayelord Hauser, whose book *Look Younger, Live Longer* was third on the nation's non-fiction bestseller list in 1950 and led the list in 1951.

Hauser, born Helmut Eugene Benjamin Gellert Hauser in Tübingen, Germany, in 1895, sold his dietary ideas to the Hollywood movie colony in the late 1920's and 'thirties. He had no medical or nutritional education, but Hauser charmed such deep thinkers as Lady Elsie Mendl, the Duchess of Windsor, Queen Alexandra of Yugoslavia, Baron Philippe de Rothschild, Cobina Wright, Sr., and Paulette Goddard into endorsing his views. And he no doubt had an influence on the influential Gloria Swanson.

Hauser's book cited a medical journal which claimed that "seventy-five per cent of the senior half of our population suffers from malnutrition." To overcome "a number of nutritional deficiencies" which lead to "premature aging," Hauser campaigned not only for large intakes of vitamins and minerals, but also for such food factors as yeast nucleic acid, which—along with pyridoxine (vitamin B_6) and pantothenic acid—can be found, Hauser said, in such "wonder foods" as brewers' yeast.

Other wonder foods on Hauser's list include powdered skim milk, yogurt, wheat germ and blackstrap molasses, the dark sticky dregs left by the sugar refining process. Blackstrap molasses, said Hauser, will help cure insomnia, menopause troubles, nervousness, baldness and low blood pressure. It will aid the digestion, help restore gray hair to its original color, strengthen the heart, help the glands to function properly and prevent many changes associated with old age.

The geriatric set has always been most susceptible to such

promises, largely because older people tend to have digestive troubles (the musculature of their stomachs, small intestines and colons often loses some of its tonus; their gastric juices often lose some of their volume, acidity and pepsin content). Older people often fail, too, to maintain proper diets; they eat too many carbohydrates (which are cheap, easy to chew and require no preparation). They are misguided by myths into avoiding milk (they think it is gassy, or constipating) and fruits (regarded as "acidy"). Or they get the idea they do not need much food because they are inactive. Often they follow quack diet ideas and take unnecessary vitamin supplements (which they can ill afford) beyond the point where medical advice and sound nutritional practices can help them.

Some food faddists prescribe grape juice for cancer, honey and vinegar for arthritis, garlic for high blood pressure, alfalfa powder for diabetes. Gelatin, they say, will give you strong fingernails, beets will give you red blood. It is all baloney.

The preachings of men like Hauser, abetted by confidence-weakening government actions (the recent "chickenfurter" decision is a case in point), have given rise to a health food business which, according to the *Wall Street Journal,* is a billion-dollar business in the U.S.

Part of this craze is based on the "soil depletion" myth. The nutritional values of the foods we eat, according to this apocrypha, have been depreciated as the fertility of the soil has been exhausted.

Farm animals, it is true, are sometimes affected by deficiencies or excesses of certain elements in the soil; this is because farm animals are so often fed on such a limited number of plant species grown on soil in a very confined area. Even with those limitations, the calcium content of cows' milk remains essentially the same no matter what the level of calcium in the cow's diet. The truth of this has been repeatedly documented.

Most people, certainly in the United States, have such a variety of meats, fish, cereals, fruits and vegetables in their diets that examples of human malnutrition due to soil deficiencies are virtually non-existent.

Soil fertility will determine how many plants will grow in a given area of land and how large the plants will grow, but for all practical purposes of human nutrition, the content of the soil will have little if any effect on the composition of plant foods grown on that soil.

In the case of vitamin C in tomatoes, in fact, poor soil may be a positive blessing. The vitamin C content depends mostly on how much sunlight strikes the fruit just before it is picked, and how intense the sunlight is. If the soil is too fertile, the tomato plants will produce large leaves that will shade the fruit with the result that it will be lower in vitamin C.

THAT "ORGANIC" BALONEY

There are unquestionably dangers of contamination from insecticides in foods, and the run-off of fertilizers into streams may jeopardize fishlife, but while some pesticide and herbicide residues may indeed be carcinogenic it is hardly true, as claimed by "organic farming" exponents, that the use of "artificial" fertilizers, weed killers and insect sprays are behind the majority of America's health disorders, including cancer. DDT has not yet been shown to have harmful effects for humans except as it affects fish and wildlife. More and more curbs are being imposed on the use of DDT, and on some herbicides as well. Use of the weed-killer 2,4,5-T was limited in late October, 1969, by the federal government after it was shown that relatively large doses of it, fed during pregnancy to mice and rats, evidently cause the animals to produce offspring with more than the usual percentage of birth defects.

But the opposition to chemical herbicides and pesticides is not the central issue with the organic farming crowd.

Their leading spokesman for years was J. I. Rodale of Emmaus, Pennsylvania, whose 1948 book *The Organic Front* promoted methods developed by Sir Albert Howard in India for growing food without modern fertilizers. Rodale went on to develop the monthly magazines *Organic Gardening and Farming* and *Prevention*. The latter, now edited by Rodale's son Robert, tells readers how to prevent illness by eating health foods and "organically" grown foods. Its pages are full of glowing testimonials and case-histories, backed by selected research studies that support "organiculture" claims.

Most studies refute the claims. There are environmental hazards in nitrate fertilizers used to excess. But efficient agriculture depends on such fertilizers, and the developing countries desperately need them to increase food production and avert famine. As more and more good farmland disappears under concrete, organic farming becomes an increasingly unrealistic anachronism.

Health food shops get healthy prices for organically grown produce, which many people buy because it "tastes better" or is "more nutritious." Often it does taste better than supermarket produce, not because it is organically grown but because it comes from varieties selected for flavor, is naturally ripened and is either sold locally or shipped by air instead of through slow, normal marketing channels. Factors of freshness can mean marginally higher amounts of vitamin C, but otherwise vitamin and mineral content varies little between food plants grown with organic compost, animal manure and crushed rock fertilizers and those grown with properly administered inorganic nitrates, potash and phosphates. Plants cannot absorb the elements of organic fertilizers until soil bacteria break them down into inorganic form.

Yet "organically grown" remains a magic phrase in the

health food shops of America and Great Britain, shops whose proprietors thrive on the credibility gap which exists on many levels of modern society but which comes closest to home when it concerns what people eat.

EXPLOITERS OF DOUBT

Preachers of wild-eyed gospels continue to find willing listeners, medical and nutritional advances notwithstanding.

Nutrition is still a young science, but it has come a long way and is going farther all the time to sort out mysteries of nutrients and their functions in human physiology. The gaps in nutritional knowledge are still filled by false prophets whose credentials are little better than those of Horace Fletcher, William Howard Hay or Gayelord Hauser.

One reason the purveyors of irresponsible misinformation about foods find such a rich seedbed for their Mickey Mouse products and proclamations is the communications problem which confronts the FDA, the Department of Agriculture and other responsible bodies. The pronouncements of the legitimate authorities, based on solid research and careful evaluation of the best possible relevant data, are not as a rule sensational. They do not make large headlines. They do not appear over and over again in various ways in various underground media as do the wilder assertions of the iconoclasts.

Not every research finding issued by the "Establishment" is necessarily the final and absolute truth. All "truths" are subject to constant re-examination. Yet one error, or one reversal of position, on the part of an official agency is taken by millions of people as evidence that nothing the agency says can be trusted—which somehow gets turned round to mean that whatever is published by irresponsible sources *can* be trusted.

The uproar over cyclamates helps to illustrate the point.

The removal of cyclamates from the FDA's GRAS list and from the market should not shatter the credibility of all FDA rulings or confirm the notions of the extremists. Unfortunately, it will have that effect for some people.

The undercover sniping by health food elements at the medical Establishment and at official government agencies falls within the sanctuary of freedom of speech. But it poses a dilemma. Occasional reassurances by public officials are no match for the virulence of inadequately documented assertions which appeal to popular emotions.

Carlton Fredericks, who has built a career as a "nutrition authority" with a radio program, a publication, lectures and several popular books, is a paramount example of the food-lore extremists who see "betrayal" in every supermarket.

It was Fredericks who crusaded so vociferously against the use of BHT as an antioxidant; he remains unconvinced by the judgment of the World Health Organization and the FAO, a judgment based on opinions of men with better credentials than Carlton Fredericks'.

Fredericks rests his arguments heavily on the idea that each of us is an individual and the "average" established requirement of any vitamin or mineral or other nutrient may not be adequate in our particular health circumstances.

No one can argue with that. Tolerances, allergies and bodily needs are all very individual things. The fact of individual variations, however, does not justify assertions that boosting intake of certain vitamins and minerals, some of which have not been recognized as having any nutritional value at all, can ward off gray hair, prevent cancer, cure sterility or hypothyroidism or arthritis.

Fredericks was arrested back in 1945 and charged with practicing medicine without a license. He pleaded guilty in Special Sessions Court in New York City and paid a $500 fine. It was either that or spend three months in jail.

A more flagrant case of quackery is that of Adolphus

Hohensee as related in James Harvey Young's book, *The Medical Messiahs*. Like Gayelord Hauser, Hohensee gave health lectures to promote health foods, but he was less of a charm boy than Hauser. He put an M.D. after his name, even though he had had only one semester of high school. A big, balding man with a waxed black moustache, Hohensee was a caricature of a pitchman. But his partisans were fierce in their adherence to his claims.

The normal diet, said Hohensee, eroded the kidneys, stagnated the blood, corroded the blood vessels, clogged the intestines. His diet, on the other hand, could rebuild all the body's organs except the kidneys, could dissolve incrustations in the brain that prevented clear thinking and could dissolve incrustations between the laminations of the eyeballs, thus making eyeglasses unnecessary.

This last claim is reminiscent of Stan Freeburg's crack about the advertising slogan used for some years by the Tea Council. "Take tea and see," said the Council. "You mean I can throw away my glasses?" asked Freeburg.

Hohensee revived the old myth that aluminum cooking utensils poisoned food. Milling cereals, pasteurizing milk and canning foods destroyed the natural nutrients, he said. He quoted the Bible freely and used big scientific words to impress his listeners. But once he got going, he promised people they could live to 180 by using his products and invited them to join him on man's first trip to the moon.

After five years of coining money at this game, Hohensee was arrested and tried in Phoenix in 1948. The foreman of the jury was a local merchant named Barry Goldwater. Hohensee paid an $1800 fine. Six years later he was convicted again, this time in Scranton, Pennsylvania. While his lawyers were appealing his case, Hohensee was caught by newspaper photographers at a back table in a Houston restaurant. He was eating fried red snapper (he had often said that frying destroys the good qualities of food) and slices of white French bread (he had said white bread "knots in a ball in your stomach and stays there in a big lump") and guzzling beer.

This modern medicine man finally went to jail in the spring of 1957 and served a year and a day. In 1962 he was sentenced by a California judge for selling honey, which he called "ambrosia of the gods" and promoted with his usual curative promises. The judge suggested Hohensee be put in charge of the prison's beehives. But after eighteen months behind bars Adolphus' conviction was reversed on an appeal that the evidence in the case had been falsely secured. Hohensee was soon back in business, frightening people with talk about the "Marble Orchard," teasing them about their sex lives ("The sex act," he declared, "should last for one hour."), and spreading the myths that most diseases stem from improper diet, that modern foods are lacking in vitamins and minerals because the soil is depleted, that foods are poisoned by chemical fertilizers and that everyone needs diet supplements to be healthy.

. . . .

DIETS FOR LOVERS

Less menacing than the diet evangelists, though often overlapping them, are those "authorities" who specify this food or that as beneficial to virility, or as "aphrodisiacs."

Back in the Middle Ages, coffee was called the "black enemy of sleep and copulation." If copulation had an enemy in coffee, it had alleged allies everywhere else through history.

The Old Testament mentions the mandrake root, a cousin of the potato and the tomato. The Greeks used the carrot as "love medicine" and called it "Philtron." They credited the leek ("Storgethron") with powers of venery, too. Pliny echoed the Old Testament's mandrake root and also prescribed the snout and foot of the hippopotamus to increase sexual potency. Ovid listed a number of aphrodisiacs of his time:

> Pepper with biting nettle-seed they bruise
> With yellow pillitory wine infuse . . .
> Eat the white shallots sent from Megara
> Or garden herbs that aphrodisiac are,
> Or eggs, or honey on Hymettus flowing,
> Or nuts upon the sharp-leaved pine trees growing.

Horace spoke of dried marrow and liver as being popular love foods of his era. Petronius and others in the next century recommended the pitch from a branch of the pomegranate tree, the testicles of an ass, intestines of various birds and fish, oysters and other shellfish, frogs, parts of reptiles, mushrooms, fava beans, snails, onions and snails' heads with sauce.

The peoples of the Near East and the Orient have always been particularly susceptible to aphrodisiac claims; in 1907 the Kamashastra Society (Paris and Benares) published a translation by Sir Richard Burton of *The Perfumed Garden for the Soul's Delectation,* a celebrated work on the subject by the Shaykh Nafzawi.

Among other things, Nafzawi said, "he who boils asparagus, and then fries them in fat, and then pours upon them the yolks of eggs with pounded condiments, and eats every day of this dish, will grow very strong for coitus, and find in it a stimulant for his amorous desires."

Brillat-Savarin wrote in *The Physiology of Taste* that the truffle can "make women more tender and men more apt to love."

Ah, those Frenchmen! Absinthe, a liqueur made from wormwood and outlawed even in France since 1915 (it can cause blindness, insanity and death), was long prized by the

French for its aphrodisiac powers, real or imagined.

But seafood probably has the most enduring reputation as an aid to lovemaking.

One story, retold by Brillat-Savarin, goes back to the days of the Crusades. The Sultan Saladin supposedly locked up some celibate dervishes to test their ascetic will power. He fed them well on a diet of meat and then presented them with "two odalisques of surpassing loveliness [but the] saints emerged from their soft ordeal as pure as the diamond of Visapoor." Then Saladin put the men on a diet of fish and exposed them once again to the temptations of the flesh, "and this time the two happy cenobites succumbed most marvelously."

In *Tableau de l'Amour,* written in the seventeenth century, Dr. Nicolas Venette put it this way: "We have observed in France that those who live almost entirely on shellfish and fish . . . are more ardent in love than others. In fact, we ourselves feel most amorously inclined during Lent."

Roy de Groot quotes the poet Monselet on the powers of *bouillabaisse,* that fish stew the Greeks call *psaro,* the Italians *zuppa di pesce* and the Belgians *Ghentsche waterzooie.* Wrote Monselet:

> And chilly beauties, not a few,
> Will do whate'er you wish,
> Partaking, tête-a-tête with you,
> Of this perfidious dish.

Some ancient cults encouraged their people to eat great amounts of fish, but forbade priests, who were supposed to be celibate, to eat any at all.

And in the United States today the Oyster Institute of North America distributes posters which read, "Eat Oysters: Love Longer."

Aphrodisiac powers have been ascribed to crabs, caviar,

crayfish tails and shark fin soup, the last being a classic Chinese love potion.

Some of the most innocent foods have at various times been credited with remarkable powers—potatoes, for example. In seventeenth-century Europe, when the potato was eyed with such suspicion, one writer said, "Eating of these roots doth excite Venus and increaseth lust." The idea is widely echoed in various surviving writings of the time.

What other foods have been alleged to have aphrodisiac effects? If we take seriously diverse claims made at different times in history, the list is endless.

To arouse Louis XV, Madame DuBarry is supposed to have used truffled sweetbreads, venison, pheasant cooked in white wine, capon in sherry broth and various vegetables, herbs and spices. James Boswell thought ambergris from whales was effective. The Dutch gynecologist Van de Velde (author of *Ideal Marriage*) favored celery, artichokes and asparagus on the ground that the acids they contain are filtered and eliminated separately by the kidneys and excite the urinary passages.

But all of the following, and more, have been cited at one time or another as aphrodisiacs: anise, avocados, beans, raw beef, white beets (named by Pliny along with asparagus, dill, licorice and hyena eyes), birds' nest soup, carrots, cheeses of various kinds (notably Parmesan), chocolates and cocoa (forbidden to their women by the Aztecs and to seventeenth-century monks by Jean Franco Raucher), chutneys, cloves, Coca-Cola, eels, eggs (especially raw eggs), fennel, garlic, honey, hot sauces, various kinds of mushrooms (particularly the morel), mutton with caraway seed, nutmeg, olives, peas, peppermints and peppermint oil (mentioned by Aristotle), pimentos, pistachio nuts, radishes, saffron, thyme, tomatoes (those dangerous "love apples") and vanilla.

Joseph Wood Krutch, who mentions capsicums (peppers), observes delicately that "the number of things credited with this characteristic suggests that a ready spontaneity is often attributed to some artificial stimulant."

People who subscribe most to the idea of aphrodisiac foods and virility diets are people who live in countries where diet deficiencies are common. Their ordinary diets in many cases simply do not provide the normal animal energy and vitality required for healthy sexual activity—or any other kind of activity. One hesitates to cite Gayelord Hauser as an authority for anything, but he must be right in saying that "When nutritional deficiencies have been overcome, improved health and vigor will be reflected in greater virility and normal libido." Viva libido. In the absence of extraordinary physical or psychological factors to the contrary, Hauser has to be correct.

Livestock breeders, for whom sexual performance is a gut matter of dollars and cents, have noted that a low plane of nutrition limits sperm production in rams, boars and bulls. Severe restriction of protein, vitamin A or calorie intake impairs also the production of the male sex hormone testosterone, which is manufactured both by the testicles and by the adrenal glands, but the restriction has to be severe. Excessive calorie intake can be another deterrent to satisfactory male reproductive performance, animal breeders have found.

As for females, heifers raised on protein-deficient diets do not go into heat (or, as the breeders put it, "show no symptoms of estrus"). Their ovaries and uterus remain infantile. Phosphorus deficiency, or reduced phosphate utilization due to a high calcium intake, can produce "irregular estrus" and eventually stop the heifer from going into heat at all. Vitamin A, B_{12} and E deficiencies can also interfere with female animals' sexual health.

A final discrediting note about aphrodisiac foods is the very number and diversity of prescriptions for "sexually stimulating" comestibles. History, after all, can produce a

similar list of items used with little success for purposes of
contraception, including peas, asparagus, marjoram, rose-
mary, thistle (in North America), green coconut (in the Pacific
islands) and pineapple (in Malaya). None did a thing to slow
the multiplication of the human race.
. . . .

There are many books of aphrodisiac recipes, but one in-
gredient is conspicuously missing from them all: any "aphrodisiac" must certainly be taken with a grain, at least, of
salt.

As the French gastronome and food columnist Robert
Courtine says, "The mouth is not used only for eating, and a
good meal puts you in the mood. They say wine is good for
women when men drink it, and they say the same of eating
artichokes."

Not only Frenchmen but all men (and women, too) have a
basic appetite for sex as for food. The first appetite can
hardly be satisfied without sufficient bodily nourishment.
Thus does Marston Bates raise the familiar objection to
Freudian psychology that "its emphasis on sex comes from
its basis in Western culture where sex is scarce—or at least
strictly controlled—while food is reasonably abundant and
generally available."

Bates recalls the studies of a British anthropologist, Au-
drey Richards, who explored human relations in an African
tribe where the sex-food balance was quite the reverse of the
Western balance. She found that culture and tradition governed food behavior much more than they did sexual behavior, leading Bates to comment that "even in our own society food behavior is subject to all sorts of taboos and controls." The reason these have not been studied more
thoroughly by psychologists and sociologists, Bates suggests, is
that "we tend to find sex more fascinating than food—I suppose because we have more trouble with it."

No need to go to Africa to find a reverse in the relative
importance of sex and food. Friends confined during the
war to prisoner-of-war camps under near-starvation condi-

tions tell us their fantasies then revolved around food, not sex. As for sex being more fascinating than food, M. Courtine reminds us that "cooking is the only area where you can still invent. In sex we know all the positions—it's limited. But in cooking there are unexplored regions—bitter-sweet, *chaud-froid,* cold goose with hot sliced potatoes, texture."

At the rate the human race has multiplied to crowd the earth—and jeopardize its ability to feed itself (half the world even now is undernourished or actually hungry)—the last thing we would seem to need is an aphrodisiac food. But nobody should be confused by the fact that birth rates are highest in the starving countries of the world: a couple need have sexual relations. . .but once a year for the reproductive apparatus to operate at close to maximum capacity.

The truth about aphrodisiac foods, however, is that their major function is to serve as entertainment, like the fried grasshoppers sold in cans at supermarkets. They are related, in a reverse way, to saltpeter, a subject of schoolboy bull sessions for as long as anyone can remember.

Boys have long speculated that saltpeter was being added to their food for the purpose of dampening their youthful lubricity. How the rumor began is anybody's guess, but it has no basis in fact. Saltpeter, or saltpetre, is potassium nitrate; it is a white salt used to some extent as a meat preservative and used more widely in the manufacture of gunpowder, fireworks and dynamite. But it does no more to cool a young man's explosive sexual appetite than mandrake root, tomatoes, cocoa, artichokes or oysters will do to inflame or sustain those appetites.

EATING ASTROLOGICALLY

There is no law against believing that "wonder foods" will keep you young, that aphrodisiac foods will prolong or reawaken your sexual vitality, or even that the zodiac sign of your birthday determines what you should eat.

Astrology is an ancient mystic "science," originally Egyptian and Middle Eastern; it is based on the questionable premise that people born in different calendar periods share certain qualities and characteristics. We are all governed, say the astrologists, by different planets, the calendar periods of our birthdays being represented by such symbols as a ram, a bull, twins, a crab, a lion, a virgin, a balance scale, a scorpion, an archer or centaur, a goat, a water bearer and two fish.

Anyone born under a certain zodiac sign is said to have tendencies toward certain diseases. And just as a person is "ruled" by a given planet (e.g., Mars in the case of Aries, Venus in the case of Taurus, Uranus for Aquarius), various foods are also "ruled" by these planets (e.g., Mars controls most of the spices, Venus controls apples, almonds, apricots, grapes, figs, peaches, wheat and sweet-smelling spices, Uranus controls—well, that is the general idea).

According to this elaborate design, the best vitamin A sources for an Aries are milk, cheese, butter, fish oils, green leaf vegetables (especially escarole), yellow vegetables (sweet potatoes, carrots), okra pods, watercress, alfalfa herb, lettuce and fruits with yellow flesh.

But for an Aquarius in this Age of Aquarius, the best vitamin A sources are whole milk products, seafoods, fish liver oils, liver, lamb, green leaf vegetables, kale, yellow vegetables and fruits with yellow flesh, and salad greens.

It is perfectly possible, however, to be an Aries who is allergic to vegetables in the carrot family, or an Aquarius with an intolerance for milk products. The astrologists no doubt have glib answers to those problems, but their "science" is as modern as Hippocrates, who required his fourth-century B.C. students to study astrology because no science at the time was any better.

In this anti-rational age too many people still prefer to avoid the truths established by science and to pursue any food fad that comes along, however discredited its proponents, however unlikely its claims. It is the Age of Aquarius.

23 Pat O'Brien Movies

Bruce Jay Friedman

This one time, there was no agonizing wait for patrol cars to filter through jammed midtown traffic. And no one in the crowd had cause to remark, "Just try to get a cop when you need one." In fact, there wasn't any crowd. The police got there before one had time to gather, and within seven minutes after the young man had taken his place on the sixteenth-story hotel-room ledge, a patrolman named Goldman with warm eyes and curly hair was out on the ledge with him, just four feet away.

The young man was thin and muscular and his back was curved into a question mark. He wore a flapping T-shirt with a large hole in the center. Beneath the T-shirt a square patch of bandages showed. It was a gray day in March, the first time the wind had blown seriously, and it seemed to be making up for all the other windless days of the month. The patrolman slouched back casually against the building wall, took off his hat and, making a pained face, scratched his head with one finger. Then he lit a cigarette.

"All right," said the young man, "let me tell you right now, I know the whole bit. I mean the casual thing you're pulling with the head-scratching and the we're-just-two-fellows-out-here-having-a-chat routine. I've seen it in a million Pat O'Brien movies. They picked you because you're a family man and you know I have a family and that's the way to work it with me, right? First I get a cigarette to relax me, then I hear about your kids, and we go into a little life-can-be-beautiful, right? If I act real serious, then you say, 'I dare you to jump, show-off. If you really want to jump, you'd have done it long ago.' Right? Okay, let me tell *you* something. I'm going. I'm not showing off, I'm not waiting for any crowds. You got an empty house or standing room only, I'm going. Twenty minutes go by on the clock, and I'm off this ledge like a shot. Give me that 'Go ahead and jump' routine and I'm not waiting the twenty."

The patrolman scratched his head again and said, "No, I'm not going to tell you to go ahead and jump because . . ."

"I'm too bright," said the young man. "Because I got too good a head on my shoulders, right? And any guy with such brains shouldn't be getting ready to take a dry dive, right? Oh, you're cute, very cute. How many times have they sent you out on these? You must be the champ of the whole police department. With the kindness and the head-scratching. Give me a little life-can-be-beautiful."

"I didn't say it can be beautiful," said the patrolman, loosening his tie. "You did. Most of the time it stinks."

"Excellent con," said the young man. "Everybody takes the good with the bad, but the chickens commit suicide, right? You plunge for the concrete and all you're proving is what a coward you are, right? You really are the cutest in the business. How many Pat O'Brien movies did you sit through to pick up this jazz, twenty-three? And look how long you've kept me out here, too. Let me tell you something so you don't feel too cute. You haven't kept me out here one second more than I want to be here. I told you. Twenty minutes and I'm flying. Twenty minutes and I go for that sweet old concrete."

A crowd began to form now, not a giant milling crowd, but a scraggly one that really didn't seem satisfied with what was going on above. Officer Goldman spun his cap on one finger and said, "You *are* bright. I don't care what you say, you're a bright guy. And a lot of what you say makes sense."

"Do you want to do me a favor?" said the young man, hooked over in the question mark and leaning toward the patrolman. "Do you want to do one thing for me, drop the casual routine. The head-scratching, the yawning, the hat-spinning. It doesn't go. Don't you think I know it's right out of the old Pat O'Brien manual? Relax him. Yawn it up a little bit. Act like the one thing in the world you absolutely don't care about is whether he plunges or not. Try it next time, ace. You care. You got to care. What have you got, twenty-four straight? I go off this ledge, and there goes your record. Nobody, not Pee Wee Reese or Ancient Archie Moore, likes to blow a contest after twenty-four straight."

"Of course I care," said the patrolman, clamping his cap hard on his head so the wind wouldn't take it. "But I can't help it if I'm casual. I *am* casual. If I acted tense and excited, *then* I'd be acting phony."

The police lieutenant who was conducting the operation called Officer Goldman back through the hotel window and, for three minutes, while the young man hung crooked on the ledge, they conferred, and then Goldman crept back out again.

"Do you think you can handle this one?" said the young man. "Isn't that what they asked? 'You don't seem to be getting anywhere with him. Maybe there's a personality clash.' Isn't that it? Isn't that what they said? All right, look, after I dive, you tell them you were as good as anybody they could have sent out. And your record still stands, because this guy was different and nobody could have grabbed him. If you want I'll write out a little note saying this is not to count on Officer what?"

"Officer Goldman," said the patrolman.

"On Officer Goldman's record. Because this guy was different. Nobody could have grabbed him."

"I don't think you're so different," said the patrolman, looking up and studying the gray sky.

"Good move, that sky bit," said the young man. "Instead of looking down at the crowd, look up. Get his mind on onward and upward things. Sneak in a little God when he's not looking. Twenty-four straight. You must have two hundred and twenty-four straight. I don't think I'm .very different either," said the young man. "I don't say I have more troubles than your last twenty-four guys. The only thing that makes me different is that I'm stepping out into the air. You can pass me kid pictures from now till kingdom come. You can get my guard up or down and you can cigarette me until you're blind, but when that buzzer rings, I'm saying goodbye to you and hello to the pavement."

"What kind of troubles?" asked the patrolman, lighting a cigarette and not looking at the young man.

"Draw him out," said the man. "Very sneakily, get him to talk about himself and then suggest that things are always darkest before the dawn. All right, save your breath. I'll draw myself out. I don't have time to wait for your Pat O'Brien routine. My stomach's the main thing. It's been knotted up since I was ten. Six operations, and last year I started getting tired all the time, no energy—so they took out a coil of it longer than the telephone wire from here to Philadelphia. I went for another year, I'm twenty-nine now, and now I'm tired again. The thing I do is prune trees and I had a good business going, I did big estates, but now I'm too tired and I haven't got the strength to get up on anything. My stomach's the size of an aspirin box now and there isn't much can come out. I've got four kids and my wife's a bum. You bring her out here to plead with me and I'm off this ledge before you can sneeze. I've always got to go out and bring her back from places. I'm too tired now to keep grabbing her by the neck. So now she can come collect me off the sidewalk with a spoon. All right now, you tell me all the beautiful things I got to look forward to."

The patrolman loosened his collar and bit, speculatively, on a fingernail.

"All right, quit the collar routine. That means we're settling down for a long stay. You know just how long it's going to be. We're clear on that, I hope. But let's say I were to step back through the window now and let's say with my stomach I had another seven years coming to me. I mean you just tell me some beautiful reasons to stay alive the seven. Television shows? The joy of changing a diaper? I can see my wife a few times? Suppose you just tell me."

"I don't say there are that many joys," said the patrolman, soft blue eyes directly on the young man now. "You're right, I have been out on quite a few of these cases in the past. It wasn't twenty-four, but the last guys I had out here, *believe* me, had as much aggravation as you do, but I was able to convince them of the one thing I believe. Whether you have six months, one year, six years, or thirty, you're better off living. Being dead is no bargain."

"Well, thank you," said the young man, bowing deeper into his question mark. "At least we're not being casual. At least we're getting right down to it. Thank you for that. It doesn't make any difference though. I mean what you're saying is just words. You're helping me pass twenty minutes. You could be reciting the Declaration of Independence.

You're helping me pass my last twenty minutes on earth, Officer Goldman, and that's the end of your streak."

The police officer threw his cigarette down on the ledge, ground it out deliberately with his foot, and then kicked it down at the crowd which seemed now to be more respectable in size.

"Now, look, let me tell you something," he said.

"You can tell me anything, Pat, but if that buzzer rings, I'll cut you off in mid-sentence. If you're telling a joke and she sounds, I don't wait for the punch line. You tell that to the sergeant."

"Let me tell you something," said the patrolman, his face more stern than it had been. "I never get sore up here on one of these ledges, because, like you say, it pays off in casualness and I have a record to preserve. But you get me sore, not because you're on any ledge, but because you're so damned smug. You have all the answers. Now listen, I have to whisper some of this, because if anyone hears it I'm off the force."

"Good bit," said the young man. "You worked it right in there. Do you want us to put our heads together maybe, so I can hear you whisper?"

"I'll smack you in the mouth," said the patrolman.

"You'll never get close enough," said the man. "I thought we got that straight."

"All right," said the patrolman, breathing heavily. "Let me get myself together. I'm going to talk low and you can believe this or not because I don't care very much about you any more."

"Good bit," said the man. "You better hurry, though. I'm not waiting for any punch lines."

"I have the kind of heart that if the wind changes direction too quickly, it can stop on a dime and they carry me off in a box. I've been living with that kind of heart for nine years and nobody in the department knows it. This is just the right kind of work for me, isn't it? Climbing out on ledges to grab guys! But I have two years more to retirement, and I'm not *letting* it stop. You have to go out and grab your wife by the neck. I'm divorced fifteen years and I have nobody to go out and grab. Four kids? I have one son and he's with his mother. Do you know what I think of him? It's like a religion and he's the one you're supposed to worship. He stays away from me like the plague. He's supposed to visit me every six months. I haven't seen him in two years. There's just one thing. I happen to think life is worth living. You have a short time to live and one hell of a long time to be dead."

The patrolman lowered his head and the young man began to rub his arms as though the cold bothered him. "So what are you going to do when you retire?" he asked.

"I have a little place paid for in Florida," said the patrolman.

"And what are you going to do down there?" he asked. "Sit in a chair and hold your heart and wait for your son to come?"

"He'll come," said the patrolman.

"No he won't," said the young man.

"He will so," said the patrolman.

"The hell he will," said the young man.

The wind was chill now and had picked up in speed. The young man hugged himself and shifted from one foot to the other. The patrolman bent over, wiping his eyes, and the two were silent now, as though they were waiting for a bus. They stood that way for several minutes. Then the patrolman said, "The day stinks," not lifting his head.

"It's cloudier than hell," said the young man.

"I really picked the right kind of thing to do," said the patrolman, "pulling guys off ledges."

"Oh yes," said the young man. "You picked something very cute."

The young man looked across the street and as he studied the clock, the patrolman took off his jacket and put it down on the ledge.

"What's the bit now?" asked the young man.

The patrolman rolled up his sleeves very neatly, and then, with a look at the sky as though checking the weather, threw his cap off the ledge and followed it, executing, except for his legs, a perfect swan dive.

"Hey, I never saw that bit before," said the young man, coming out of his question mark to watch the patrolman as he neared the pavement and then went into it.

"What the hell do I do now?"